RISING STARS
Mathematics

Year **4**

Practice Book

Author: Paul Broadbent

ISBN: 978-1-78339-817-1
Text, design and layout © Rising Stars UK Ltd 2016

First published in 2016 by
Rising Stars UK Ltd, part of Hodder Education,
An Hachette UK Company
Carmelite House
50 Victoria Embankment
London EC4Y 0DZ
www.risingstars-uk.com

Author: Paul Broadbent
Programme consultants: Caroline Clissold, Cherri Moseley, Paul Broadbent
Publishers: Fiona Lazenby and Alexandra Riley
Editorial: Jan Fisher, Aidan Gill
Answer checker: Deborah Dobson
Project manager: Sue Walton

Series and character design: Steve Evans
Text design: Words & Pictures
Illustrations by Steve Evans

Cover design: Steve Evans and Words & Pictures

Printed by Liberduplex, Barcelona
A catalogue record for this title is available from the British Library.

Contents

Unit 1: Number and place value. 4
1a Counting 4
1b Place value 8

Unit 2: Addition and subtraction 13
2a Adding 4-digit numbers. 13
2b Subtracting 4-digit numbers 17

Unit 3: Factors and calculating 21
3a Counting in 6s, 9s and 12s 21
3b Calculating mentally .24
3c Calculating on paper .27

Unit 4: 2-D shapes, angles and symmetry 31
4a Three types of angle. 31
4b Triangles 35
4c Quadrilaterals 37
4d Symmetry 41

Unit 5: Different numbers 44
5a Counting in steps 44
5b Rounding, ordering and comparing 47
5c Roman numerals. 52

Unit 6: Applying addition and subtraction 54
6a Using mental and written methods to solve
     problems. 54
6b Bar models and bar charts 59
6c Solving problems 64

Unit 7: Fractions and decimals 66
7a Families of fractions .66
7b Decimals and equivalences 71

Unit 8: Methods for multiplying 74
8a Multiplication table facts 74
8b Three at once 78
8c Written methods 81
8d Scaling 84

Unit 9: Polygons and coordinates 87
9a Trapeziums and kites 87
9b Coordinates and translations 91

Unit 10: Number and place value in real life. . . .94
10a 25s and 1000s. 94
10b Place value and measures 97

Unit 11: Addition and subtraction problems. . .100
11a Solving problems using written methods . . .100
11b Applying methods of addition and subtraction .104

Unit 12: Decimals and fractions in real life. . .108
12a Equivalences. 108
12b Comparing and rounding decimals. 112

Unit 13: Multiplication tables 116
13a Multiplying and dividing mentally 116
13b Multiplying on paper 120
13c Scaling. 122

Unit 14: Perimeter, area and symmetry 125
14a Perimeter and area. 125
14b Perimeter and angles 129
14c Area and symmetry. 134

Number and place value

1a Counting

1 Write the missing numbers in each sequence.

a   6   8   ☐   12   ☐   16   18   ☐

b   55   ☐   45   40   ☐   ☐   ☐   20

c   8   ☐   ☐   20   24   ☐   32   ☐

d   ☐   110   ☐   90   80   ☐   ☐   50

2 Continue the jumps to show the skip counting in multiples of 3 and 6. Circle the multiples of 6.

```
      0    3    6    9   12   15   18   21   24   27   30   33   36
```

a   What is the second multiple of 3?   f   What is the fourth multiple of 6?

☐   ☐

b   What is the second multiple of 6?   g   What is the fifth multiple of 3?

☐   ☐

c   What is the third multiple of 3?   h   What is the fifth multiple of 6?

☐   ☐

d   What is the third multiple of 6?

☐   What do you notice?

e   What is the fourth multiple of 3?

☐

3 Complete this number grid.

3	6	9	12	15							
6	12	18	24								
9	18	27									

Look at the numbers in the first column: 3, 6 and 9.

a What total do you make if you add together 3 and 6? [ ]

b Does this happen in each column? Why? Try to explain your reasoning.

4 Write the missing numbers in each sequence.

a   −8   −7   −6   [ ] [ ] [ ] [ ]   −1   [ ]

b   5   4   3   [ ] [ ] [ ] [ ]   −2   [ ]

c   −10   −8   −6   [ ] [ ] [ ] [ ]   4   [ ]

d   11   9   7   [ ] [ ] [ ] [ ]   −3   [ ]

e   −20   −15   −10   [ ] [ ] [ ] [ ]   15   [ ]

f   22   17   12   [ ] [ ] [ ] [ ]   −13   [ ]

5 Write the missing numbers. Use this number line to help you.

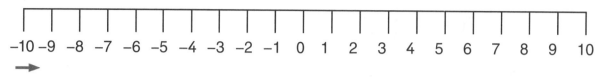
−10 −9 −8 −7 −6 −5 −4 −3 −2 −1 0 1 2 3 4 5 6 7 8 9 10

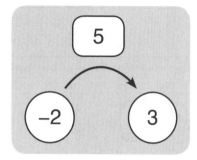
5
−2 → 3

a
[ ]
−5 → −1

b
[ ]
−3 → 0

c
[ ]
−4 → 2

d
4
−1 → ( )

e
5
( ) → −3

f
7
−2 → ( )

6 Digital roots are found by adding together the digits of a number.

For example, the digital root of 35 is 3 + 5 = 8. The digital root of 39 is
3 + 9 = 12 ➤ 1 + 2 = 3.

a Complete the charts to show the digital roots of the multiples of 3 and 6.

3 ➤ 3	6 ➤ 6	9 ➤ 9	12 ➤ 3	15 ➤ 6	18 ➤
21 ➤	24 ➤	27 ➤	30 ➤	33 ➤	36 ➤

6 ➤ 6	12 ➤ 3	18 ➤ 9	24 ➤ 6	30 ➤	36 ➤
42 ➤	48 ➤	54 ➤	60 ➤	66 ➤	72 ➤

What do you notice?

b The digital root of multiples of 9 is 9.

Is that **always true**, **sometimes true** or **never true?** Show your reasoning.

1b Place value

1 Write these numbers as words.

a 3406

b 3460

c 4036

d 6043

2 Write these as numbers.

a five thousand seven hundred and twenty

b five thousand seven hundred and twelve

c five thousand seven hundred and two

d five thousand two hundred and seventeen

e two thousand five hundred and seventy

f two thousand and fifty

3 Partition these to show the value of each digit.

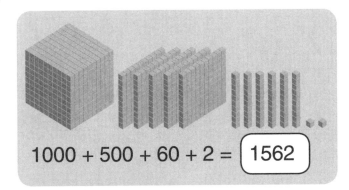

$$1000 + 500 + 60 + 2 = \boxed{1562}$$

a

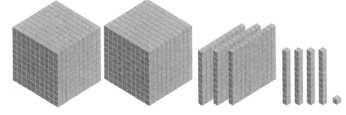

$\boxed{} + \boxed{} + \boxed{} + \boxed{} = \boxed{}$

b

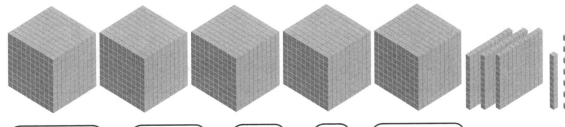

$\boxed{} + \boxed{} + \boxed{} + \boxed{} = \boxed{}$

c

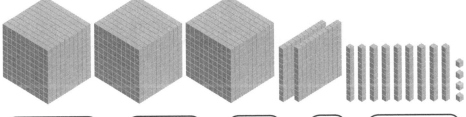

$\boxed{} + \boxed{} + \boxed{} + \boxed{} = \boxed{}$

d

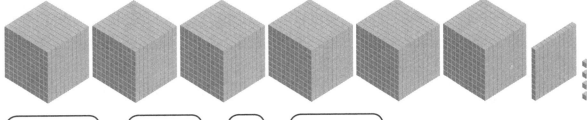

$\boxed{} + \boxed{} + \boxed{} = \boxed{}$

4 Write the numbers shown by these place-value cards.

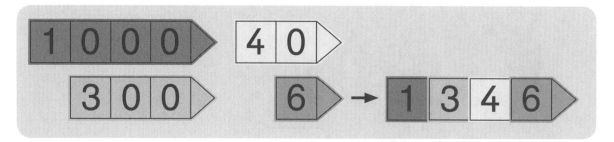

a 4295

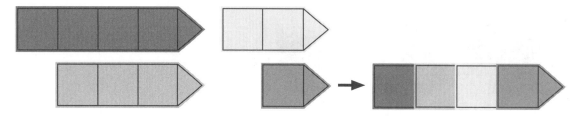

b 7813

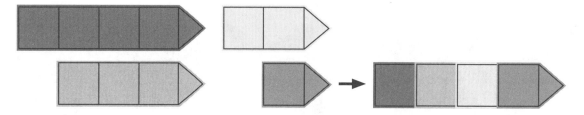

c 2064

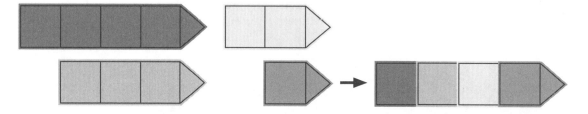

d 8401

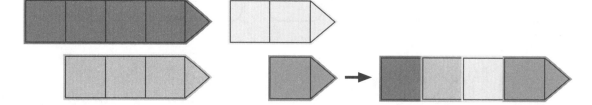

5 What is the value of the 5 digit in each of these?

a   3452 ➞ 5 × 10 = ⬚

b   1570 ➞ 5 × ⬚ = ⬚

c   582 ➞ 5 × ⬚ = ⬚

d   7405 ➞ 5 × ⬚ = ⬚

e   5009 ➞ 5 × ⬚ = ⬚

f   38.5 ➞ 5 × ⬚ or ⬚ , ⬚ or ⬚

g   200.35 ➞ 5 × ⬚ or ⬚ , ⬚ or ⬚

h   3459.26 ➞ 5 × ⬚ = ⬚

6

This abacus shows 2016.

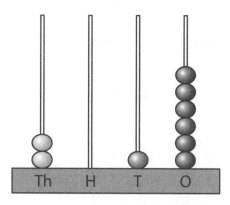

Counters can be placed on this abacus to make different numbers.

a　Only use 2 counters. Can you make 10 different numbers?

Write them in order, starting with the smallest.

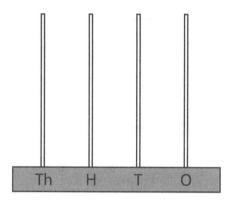

Numbers with 2 counters	Numbers with 3 counters	Numbers with 4 counters

b　Now try with 3 counters and then 4 counters. Write the numbers in order in the table. What do you notice about the numbers in the table?

Addition and subtraction

2a Adding 4-digit numbers

1 Answer each set as quickly as you can.

a	b	c	d
7 + 7 =	20 + 70 =	44 + 19 =	23 + 23 =
4 + 15 =	30 + 90 =	52 + 9 =	47 + 47 =
9 + 8 =	60 + 50 =	28 + 29 =	54 + 54 =
11 + 6 =	80 + 80 =	19 + 35 =	18 + 18 =
4 + 8 =	40 + 70 =	39 + 12 =	31 + 31 =
5 + 13 =	60 + 120 =	56 + 9 =	61 + 60 =
6 + 9 =	110 + 40 =	38 + 19 =	34 + 35 =
7 + 12 =	50 + 130 =	29 + 43 =	43 + 44 =
8 + 5 =	90 + 70 =	9 + 54 =	26 + 27 =
7 + 9 =	120 + 70 =	47 + 29 =	38 + 39 =

2 Match the pairs of numbers that total 114. One pair has been completed for you.

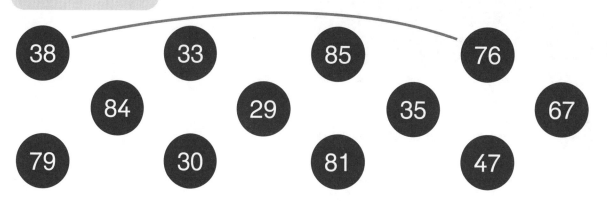

$$38 + 76 = 114$$

(38) (33) (85) (76)

(84) (29) (35) (67)

(79) (30) (81) (47)

3 Look at the number machines.

Complete each table.

IN   OUT
+29

a

IN	38		48		58		68	
OUT		50		52		54		56

IN   OUT
+2400

b

IN	1100		1500		1700		1900	
OUT		4900		4700		4500		4300

4   Answer these.

a   1827   c   1541   e   2497

   +   2740   +   2096   +   3834

       —————   —————   —————

       —————   —————   —————

b   3026   d   4560   f   1752

   +   2575   +   3643   +   6958

       —————   —————   —————

       —————   —————   —————

5 Look at these amounts and answer the questions.

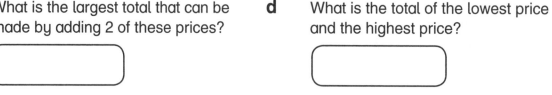

£2559 £3167 £4572 £5194 £1306

a What is the largest total that can be made by adding 2 of these prices?

d What is the total of the lowest price and the highest price?

b What is the smallest total that can be made by adding 2 of these prices?

e Which 2 prices when bought together would give a total price of £4473?

c What is the total of the 2 odd number prices?

f Which 2 prices give a total of £7739?

 6 All the digits 1 and 3 are missing.

Write the digits 1 or 3 in the correct places to complete this addition.

$$
\begin{array}{r}
4\ 6\ \boxed{\ }\ 8 \\
+\quad 9\ \boxed{\ }\ 6\ \boxed{\ } \\
\hline
\boxed{\ }\boxed{\ }\ 8\ 0\ \boxed{\ } \\
\hline
\end{array}
$$

1 Answer each set as quickly as you can.

a

17 – 8 = ☐

19 – 5 = ☐

14 – 8 = ☐

15 – 6 = ☐

19 – 7 = ☐

18 – 12 = ☐

13 – 9 = ☐

16 – 4 = ☐

18 – 13 = ☐

17 – 11 = ☐

b

120 – 60 = ☐

90 – 30 = ☐

180 – 50 = ☐

130 – 40 = ☐

160 – 70 = ☐

190 – 110 = ☐

140 – 70 = ☐

150 – 120 = ☐

110 – 80 = ☐

170 – 90 = ☐

c

22 – 19 = ☐

24 – 9 = ☐

47 – 29 = ☐

36 – 19 = ☐

44 – 9 = ☐

68 – 19 = ☐

53 – 19 = ☐

36 – 9 = ☐

81 – 29 = ☐

59 – 19 = ☐

d

32 – 26 = ☐

51 – 49 = ☐

95 – 87 = ☐

74 – 69 = ☐

41 – 38 = ☐

85 – 76 = ☐

54 – 48 = ☐

63 – 59 = ☐

96 – 88 = ☐

72 – 67 = ☐

2 Write the missing numbers on these difference grids.

a

–	56	18	64
24		6	
73	17		9
50		32	

b

–	61	9	92
57			
49		40	
15			

 3 Complete these subtractions.

a
```
   8391
 − 7157
 ──────

 ──────
```

c
```
   6732
 − 5376
 ──────

 ──────
```

b
```
   5106
 − 3691
 ──────

 ──────
```

d
```
   8544
 − 7298
 ──────

 ──────
```

4 Look at the prices and answer these questions.

Ring £156

Necklace £209

Watch £247

Earrings £119

a Mr Kite has £350 and buys the watch. How much money will he have left?

e In a sale everything is reduced by £50. Write the new price for each piece of jewellery.

b Mrs Bird has £185. How much more does she need to buy the necklace?

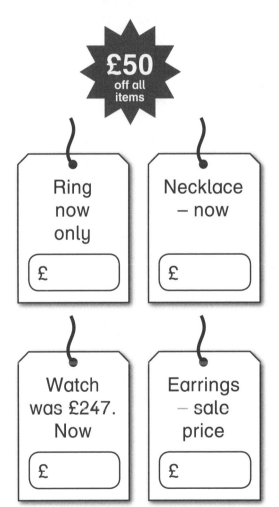

£50 off all items

c Mrs Parker has £200. How much change will she get if she buys the earrings?

Ring now only

£

Necklace – now

£

d Mr Fish has £400 and buys the watch. Does he have enough money left to buy the ring as well?

Watch was £247. Now

£

Earrings – sale price

£

5 This table shows the average depths of the deepest oceans and seas in the world.

Look at the table and answer these questions.

Ocean/sea	Average depth (metres)
Pacific Ocean	4028 m
Indian Ocean	3963 m
Atlantic Ocean	3926 m
Caribbean Sea	2647 m
South China Sea	1652 m
Bering Sea	1547 m
Gulf of Mexico	1486 m
Mediterranean Sea	1429 m

a By how many metres is the Pacific Ocean deeper than the Indian Ocean?

m

b What is the difference in depth between the Pacific Ocean and the Mediterranean Sea?

m

c What is the difference in depth between the Gulf of Mexico and the Atlantic Ocean?

m

d Which sea is 2311 m less in depth than the Indian Ocean?

e Which 2 seas have a difference in depth of 1100 m?

f Which 2 oceans or seas have the smallest difference in depth?

Factors and calculating

1

YOU WILL NEED:
* yellow colouring pencils

Follow the instructions to complete this 1–60 number grid.

1	2	3	4	5	6	7	8	9	10
11	12	13	14	15	16	17	18	19	20
21	22	23	24	25	26	27	28	29	30
31	32	33	34	35	36	37	38	39	40
41	42	43	44	45	46	47	48	49	50
51	52	53	54	55	56	57	58	59	60

Colour all the multiples of 2 yellow.

Circle all the multiples of 3.

What do you notice?

2   Look at this set of numbers.

12   54   38   60
23   72   33
18   48   16   108
56   61   42

a   Write the numbers that are multiples of 6.

b   Write the numbers that are multiples of 9.

c   Write the numbers that are multiples of 12.

3 Continue the patterns.

a

9	18	27							

b

90	81	72							

What do you notice?

4 Look at these number machines and complete each chart.

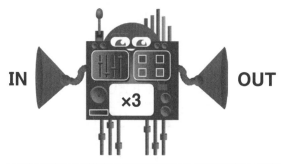

IN   OUT   ×3

a

IN	3	6	4	8	12
OUT					

IN   OUT   ×6

b

IN	3	6	4	8	12
OUT					

IN   OUT   ×9

c

IN	3	6	4	8	12
OUT					

5 A shop sells yellow tennis balls in tubes of 6 and orange tennis balls in tubes of 9.

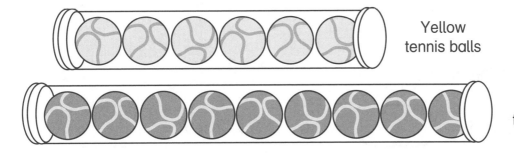

Yellow tennis balls

Orange tennis balls

A tennis club orders a total of 87 tennis balls with a mix of some orange and some yellow.

How many yellow and orange tennis balls are there in the order?

Can you find different possible answers?

6 Complete these.

a
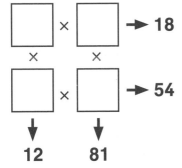

b
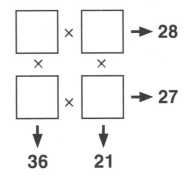

1   Answer these.

a $3 \times 5 \times 6 =$ ⬚   **e** $5 \times 2 \times 7 =$ ⬚

b $3 \times 10 \times 6 =$ ⬚   **f** $5 \times 4 \times 7 =$ ⬚

c $3 \times 2 \times 9 =$ ⬚   **g** $4 \times 5 \times 3 =$ ⬚

d $3 \times 4 \times 9 =$ ⬚   **h** $4 \times 10 \times 3 =$ ⬚

 2   Write the missing numbers.

a $4 \times$ ⬚ $\times 3 = 60$ **d** $10 \times$ ⬚ $\times 5 = 150$

b $3 \times$ ⬚ $\times 7 = 42$ **e** $4 \times$ ⬚ $\times 4 = 160$

c $2 \times$ ⬚ $\times 3 = 36$ **f** $5 \times$ ⬚ $\times 3 = 120$

 3   Answer these.

a $31 \times 2 =$ ⬚   **e** $13 \times 3 =$ ⬚

b $43 \times 2 =$ ⬚   **f** $21 \times 4 =$ ⬚

c $22 \times 3 =$ ⬚   **g** $24 \times 2 =$ ⬚

d $42 \times 2 =$ ⬚   **h** $22 \times 4 =$ ⬚

4 Multiply a number on the left by a number on the right to make each grid number.

Write the calculation in the matching square on the grid.

34

44

21

22

11

12

66	88	68
63	84	48
55	44	66

2

3

4

5

6

5 Write the signs **<** or **>** to make these correct.

a   33 × 2 ◯ 23 × 3

b   22 × 3 ◯ 32 × 2

c   32 × 3 ◯ 33 × 3

6 Try these triangle puzzles.

a Not including the number 1, find 3 numbers that make 40 when multiplied together. Write the numbers in the outside triangles. Can you find 2 sets of numbers?

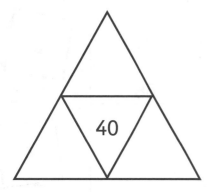 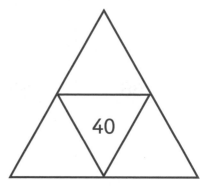

40 is an example of a 'Super-centre number' with more than one solution.

25 is an example of an 'Impossible-centre number' which cannot be made with 3 whole numbers.

b Here are 4 more triangle puzzles. Choose a number to write in the centre of your triangle. Try to find other examples of 'super' and 'impossible' centre numbers.

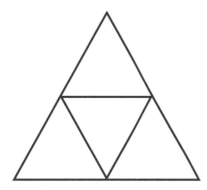 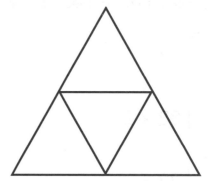

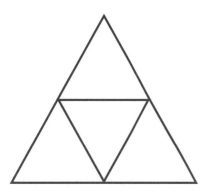 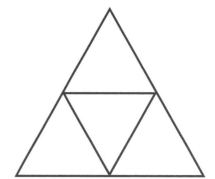

1 Write the missing numbers.

a $4 \times 9 + \boxed{} = 41$

$4 \times 9 + \boxed{} = 43$

$4 \times 9 + \boxed{} = 45$

c $3 \times \boxed{} + 4 = 40$

$3 \times \boxed{} + 4 = 37$

$3 \times \boxed{} + 4 = 34$

b $\boxed{} \times 6 + 2 = 50$

$\boxed{} \times 6 + 2 = 56$

$\boxed{} \times 6 + 2 = 62$

d $5 \times 7 + 3 = \boxed{}$

$5 \times 8 + 3 = \boxed{}$

$5 \times 9 + 3 = \boxed{}$

2 Complete these.

a $64 \times 3 = \boxed{}$

×	60	4
3			→

c $89 \times 3 = \boxed{}$

×	80	9
3			→

b $47 \times 4 = \boxed{}$

×	40	7
4			→

d $53 \times 9 = \boxed{}$

×	50	3
9			→

3 Complete these multiplications.

a 29×4 ➤ $20 \times 4 = \boxed{}$

$9 \times 4 = \boxed{}$ +

$29 \times 4 = \boxed{}$

c 35×9 ➤ $30 \times 9 = \boxed{}$

$5 \times 9 = \boxed{}$ +

$35 \times 9 = \boxed{}$

b 37×6 ➤ $30 \times 6 = \boxed{}$

$7 \times 6 = \boxed{}$ +

$37 \times 6 = \boxed{}$

d 78×3 ➤ $70 \times 3 = \boxed{}$

$8 \times 3 = \boxed{}$ +

$78 \times 3 = \boxed{}$

 4 Write each of these numbers on a small piece of paper.

YOU WILL NEED:
- **Small pieces of paper or sticky notes**

Arrange them on this multiplication.

a How many different answers can you make?

c Write the arrangement that gives you the smallest answer.

d Write the arrangement that gives you the answer nearest to 200.

b Write the arrangement that gives you the largest answer.

5 Answer these.

a Mrs Fox bought 1 table for £45 and 6 chairs at £12 each. How much did she spend altogether?

b Granny Brown took her 3 grandchildren to the cinema to watch a film. She bought 1 adult ticket for £8 and 3 child tickets at £6 each. How much did it cost for all of them to watch the film?

c A box of chocolates has 9 chocolates each with mass 20 g. The box itself weighs 35 g. What is the total mass of the box with the chocolates inside?

d Green paint is made with 5 pots of 60 g each of yellow paint and one 125 g pot of blue paint. How much green paint is made altogether?

e A film lasts 2 hours 25 minutes. What is this in minutes?

6 Multiply these and match the answer to a letter. What is the secret message?

57 × 3 ⬭

24 × 7 ⬭

19 × 9 ⬭

46 × 4 ⬭

36 × 4 ⬭

93 × 2 ⬭

17 × 9 ⬭

19 × 9 ⬭

79 × 2 ⬭

56 × 3 ⬭

57 × 3 ⬭

79 × 2 ⬭

15 × 8 ⬭

97 × 2 ⬭

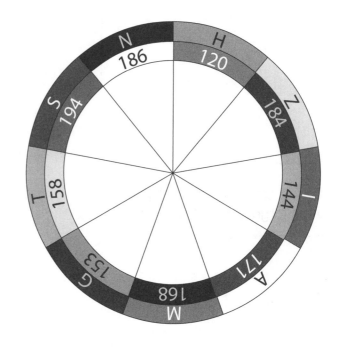

2-D shapes, angles and symmetry

4a Three types of angle

1 This dial has four positions: A, B, C and D.

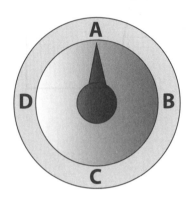

Complete this chart to show the start and finish positions for each turn.

Start position	Turn	Finish position
A	$\frac{1}{4}$ turn clockwise	B
A	$\frac{1}{2}$ turn clockwise	
A	$\frac{3}{4}$ turn clockwise	
A	$\frac{1}{4}$ turn anticlockwise	
C	$\frac{1}{4}$ turn clockwise	
C	$\frac{1}{2}$ turn anticlockwise	
D	$\frac{1}{4}$ turn clockwise	
B	$\frac{3}{4}$ turn anticlockwise	

2 Complete these.

a 1 right angle = ⬚ turn = 90°

c ⬚ right angles = $\frac{3}{4}$ turn = 270°

b 2 right angles = $\frac{1}{2}$ turn = ⬚°

d 4 right angles = whole turn = ⬚°

3 Draw small squares to show the right angles on each shape.

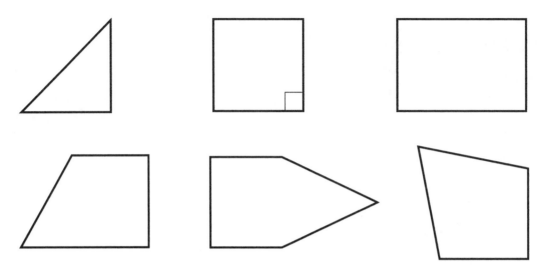

 4 How many right angles can you see on this shape?

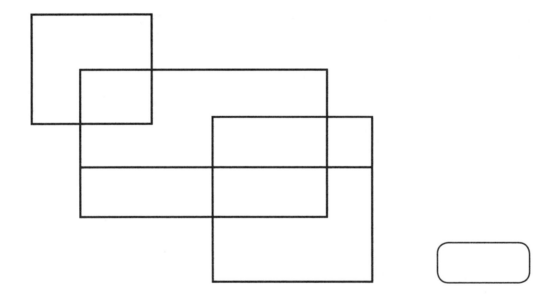

 5 Use a square corner made from folded paper to make a right angle measurer.

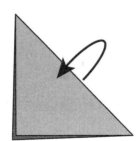

Check and name each angle below as an **acute angle**, an **obtuse angle** or a **right angle**.

a

c

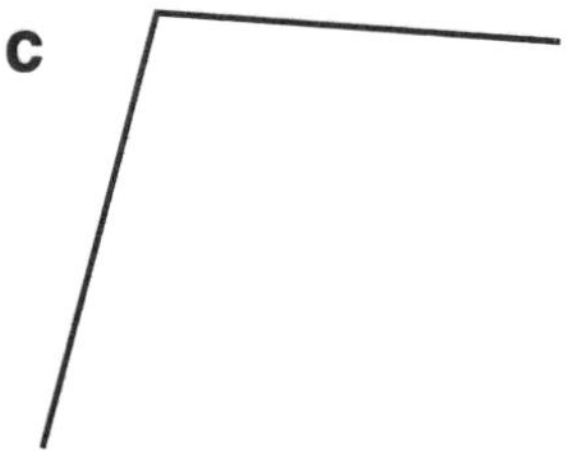

e

g

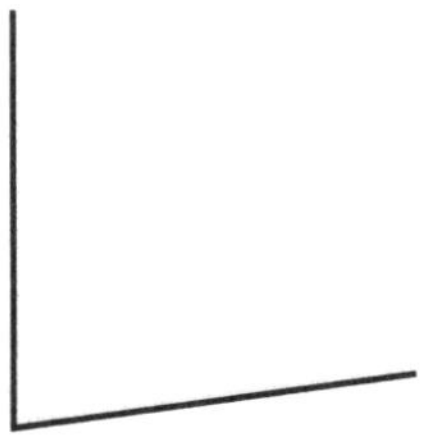

b

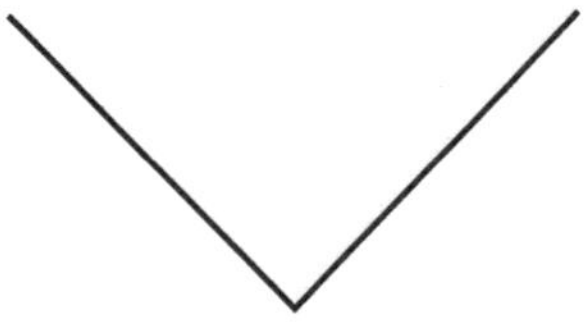

d

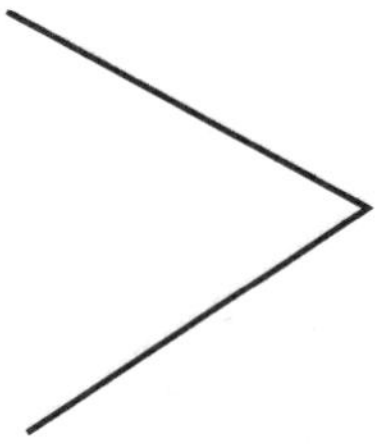

f

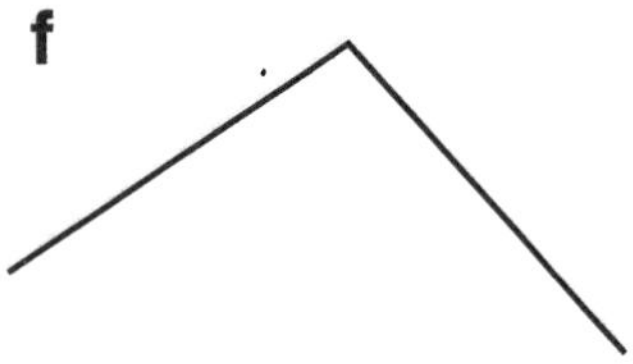

h

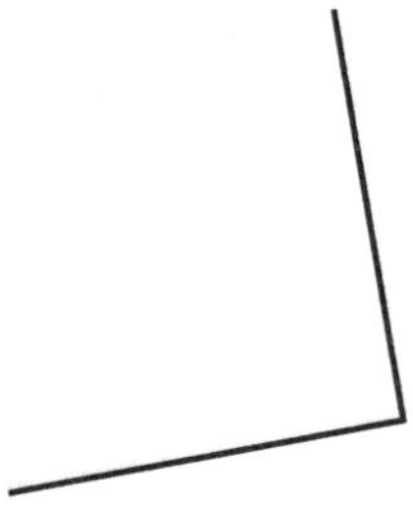

6 For each shape write the number of acute angles, obtuse angles and right angles.

a

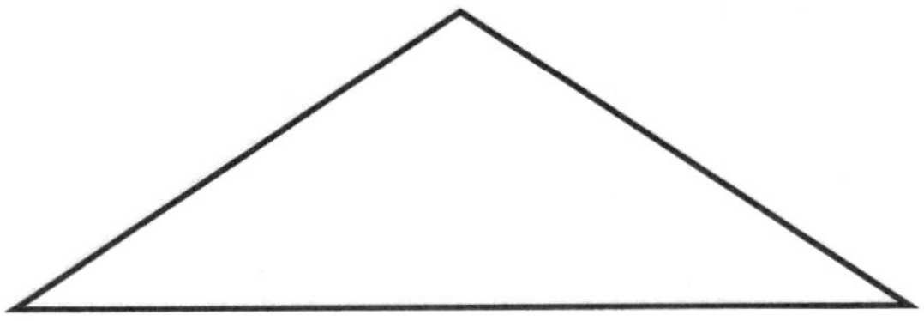

◯ acute angles

◯ obtuse angles

◯ right angles

b

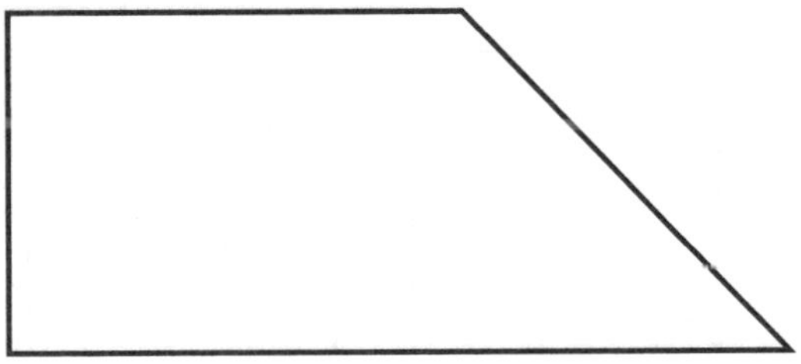

◯ acute angles

◯ obtuse angles

◯ right angles

c

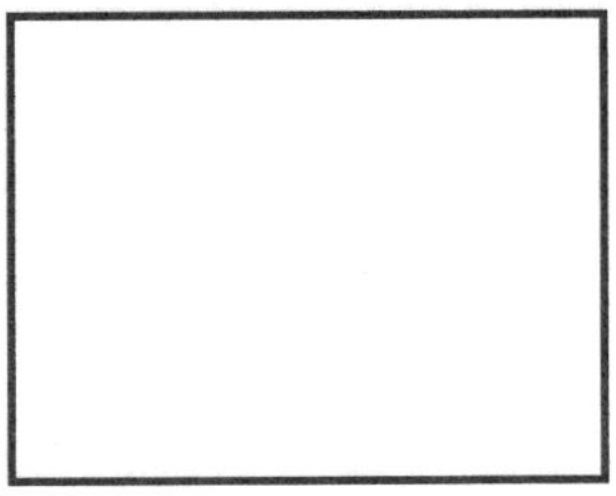

◯ acute angles

◯ obtuse angles

◯ right angles

d

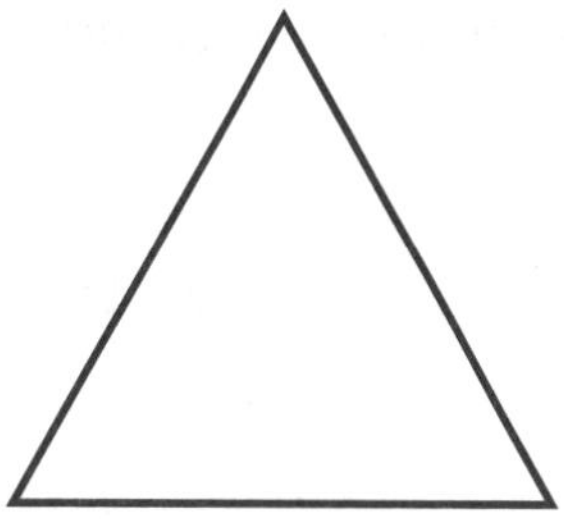

☐ acute angles

☐ obtuse angles

☐ right angles

e

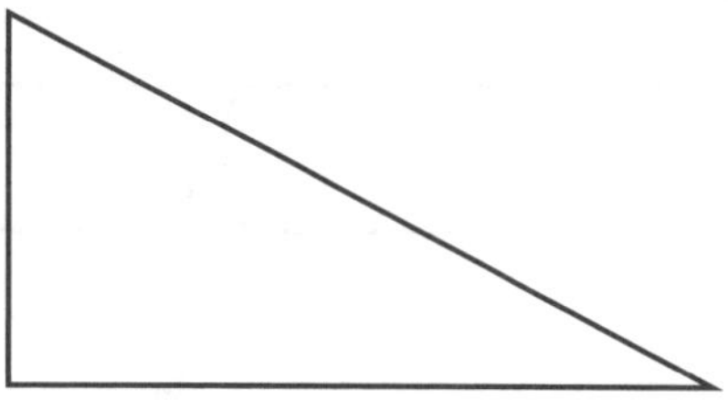

☐ acute angles

☐ obtuse angles

☐ right angles

f

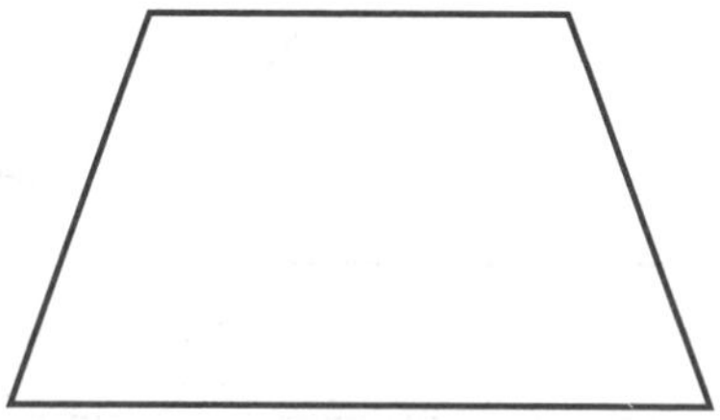

☐ acute angles

☐ obtuse angles

☐ right angles

7 These angles have been made by joining three dots.

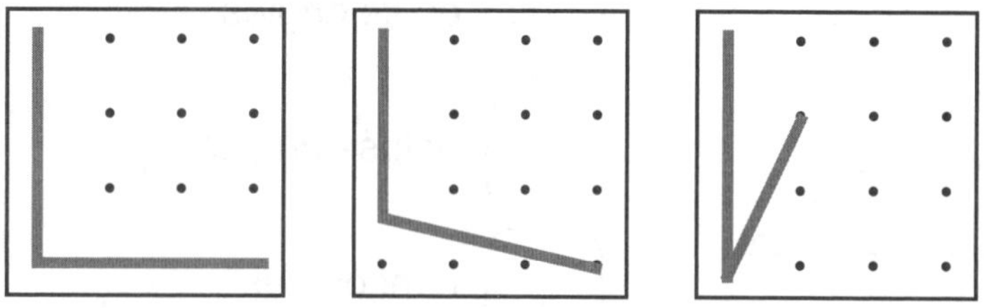

Join 3 dots on these grids. Make 2 different angles of each type.

Right angles

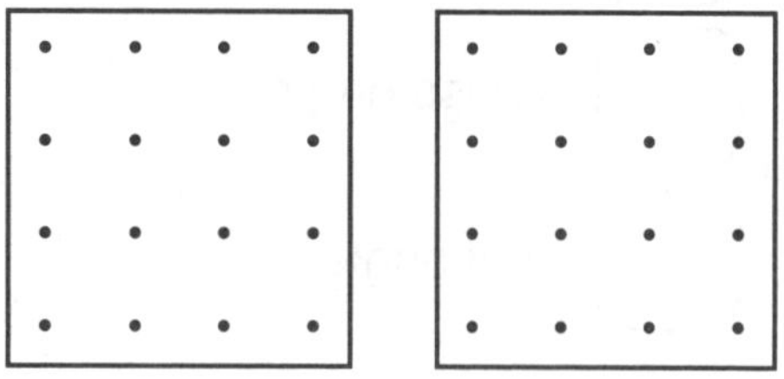

Obtuse angles

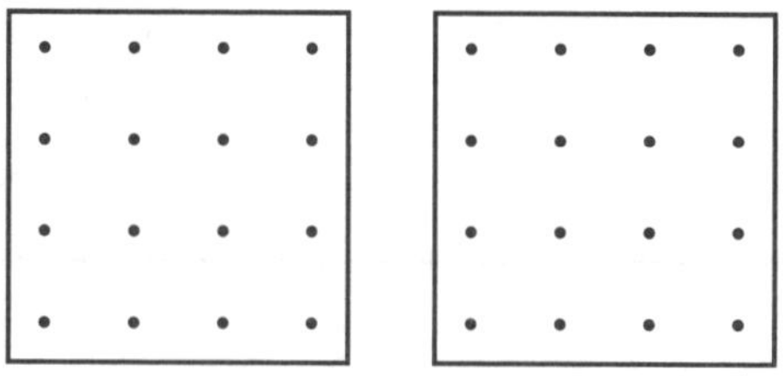

Acute angles

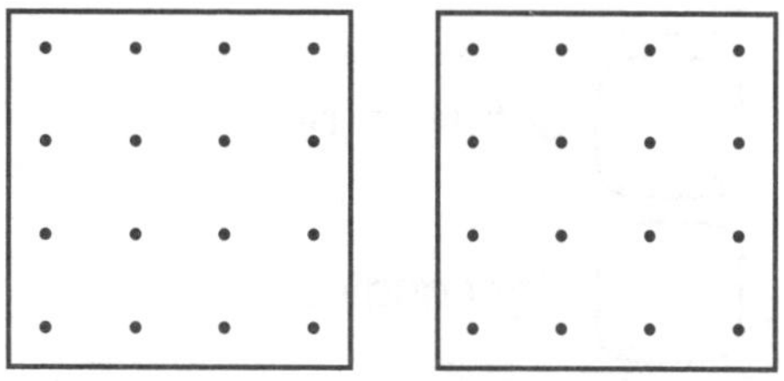

1 Use a tick, cross or circle to show each type of angle in these triangles.

Acute angle ➡ ✓   Obtuse angle ➡ ✗   Right angle ➡ 0

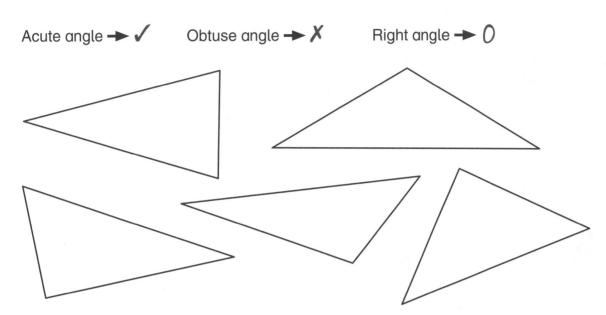

2 Look at the sets of triangles. Name each set.

A

B

C

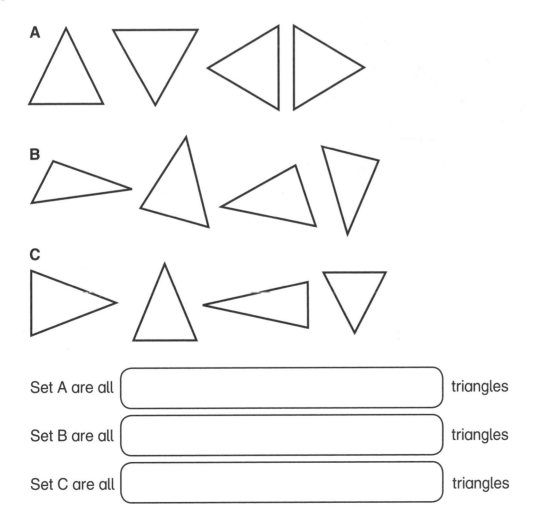

Set A are all [   ] triangles

Set B are all [   ] triangles

Set C are all [   ] triangles

3 Draw 2 more sides to complete each triangle.

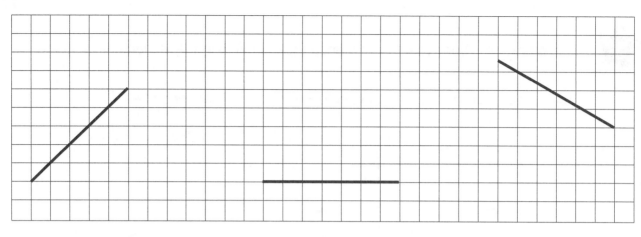

a isosceles triangle **b** equilateral triangle **c** right-angled triangle

 4 How many triangles can you count? ☐

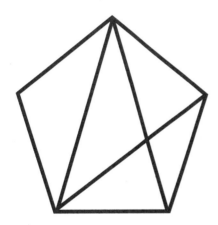

Draw your own diagram to count triangles.

⭐ **1** Name each quadrilateral.

a

quadrilateral

d

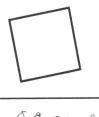

sqaure

b

rectangle

e

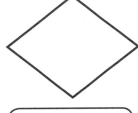

diomad

c

rectangle

f

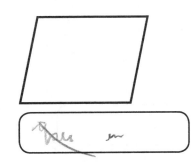

par   m

⭐ **2** For each statement draw a circle around **True or False**.

a A rhombus always has a pair of parallel lines. True False

b A rectangle always has 4 equal sides and 4 right angles. True False

c A square is a special rectangle. True False

d A parallelogram always has opposite sides of equal length. True False

e A rhombus always has pairs of opposite angles the same size. True False

These diagrams show the diagonals of 4 quadrilaterals.

Complete the shapes and write their names.

a

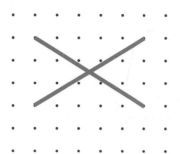

b

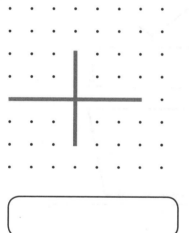

c

d

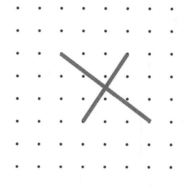

4 With 8 squares you can make 2 different rectangles.

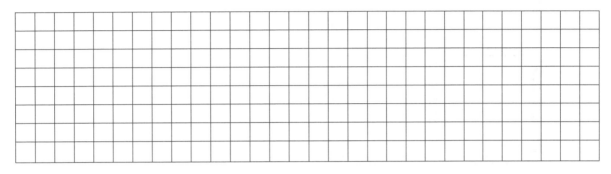

a How many different rectangles can you make with 12 squares?
Draw each different rectangle here.

b 24 squares can be arranged to make 4 different rectangles.
Investigate this to see if this is true.
Draw each different rectangle here.

Put straws or sticks in grid patterns like this.

a

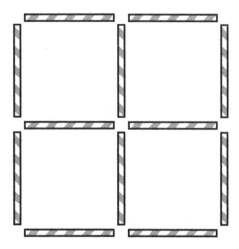

Can you see 5 squares?

Remove 2 straws and leave 2 squares.

b

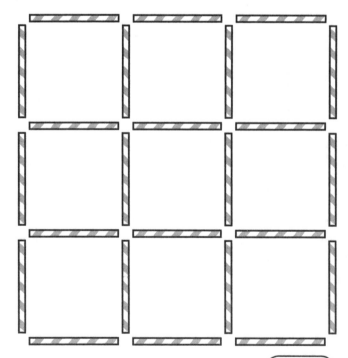

How many squares can you count?

Remove 2 straws and leave 7 squares.

1 Write either **symmetrical** or **not symmetrical** for each shape.

a

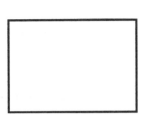

S

e

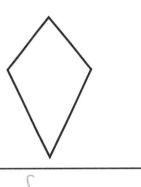

S

b

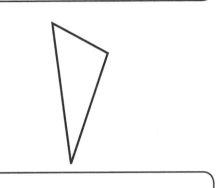

N S

f

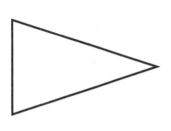

S

c

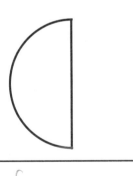

S

g

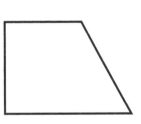

N S

d

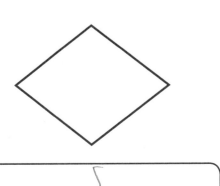

S

h

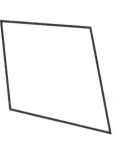

N S

2 Draw the lines of symmetry on each shape. Write how many there are for each.

a

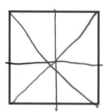

[4] lines of symmetry

e

[2] lines of symmetry

b

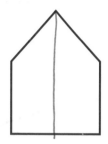

[l] lines of symmetry

f

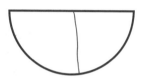

[l] lines of symmetry

c

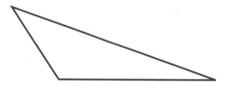

[0] lines of symmetry

g

[l] lines of symmetry

d

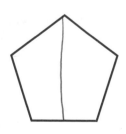

[/] lines of symmetry

h

[l] lines of symmetry

42

YOU WILL NEED:
• a ruler

Here is part of a shape.
Draw 2 more lines to make a shape
with 2 lines of symmetry. Use a ruler.

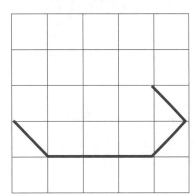

Write **Always True**, **Sometimes True** or **Never True** for each statement.

Draw examples to prove it.

a   Squares are symmetrical.

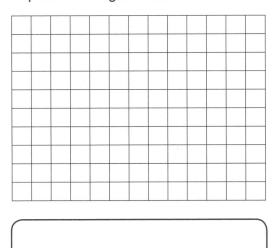

c   Rectangles have only 1 line of symmetry.

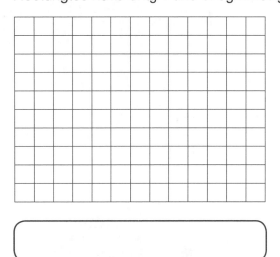

b   Triangles are symmetrical.

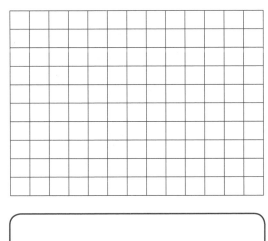

d   Parallelograms have 1 line of symmetry.

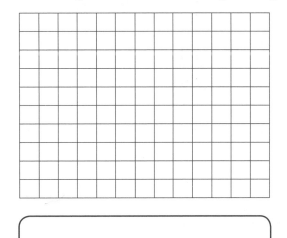

Different numbers

1 Complete the table for each function machine.

IN ×7 OUT

a

IN	3	4	7	5	6	11
OUT	21	28	5 6	63	42	77

IN ÷7 OUT

b

IN	14	42	56	63	21	49
OUT	2	6	7	9	3	6

2 Write the number that each arrow points to.

a

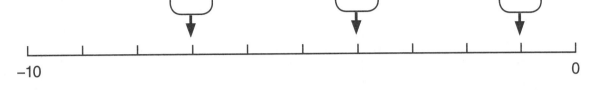

−10   0

b

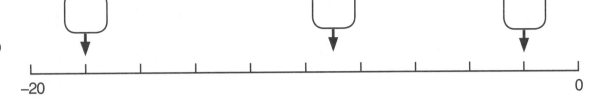

−20   0

c

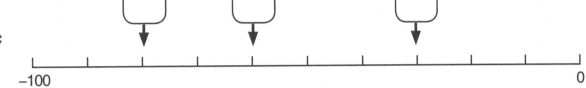

−100   0

Write the next 3 numbers in each sequence.

a

−8   −5   −2   1   4   ☐ ☐ ☐

Will 30 be in this sequence? ☐

b

−6   −1   4   9   14   ☐ ☐ ☐

Will 99 be in this sequence? ☐

c

20   14   8   2   −4   ☐ ☐ ☐

Will −30 be in this sequence? ☐

d

11   7   3   −1   −5   ☐ ☐ ☐

Will −21 be in this sequence? ☐

4 What is the difference in temperature between each pair of thermometers?

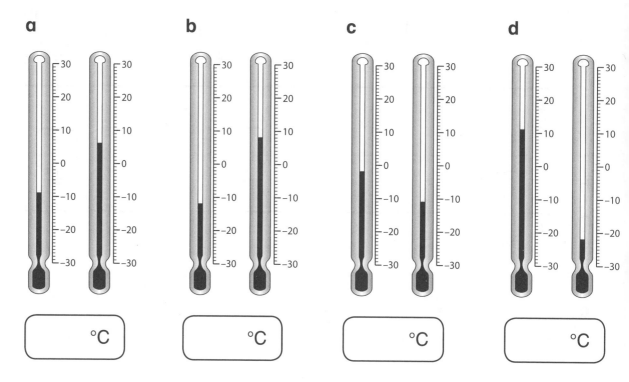

a

°C

b

°C

c

°C

d

°C

5 Write the new temperatures.

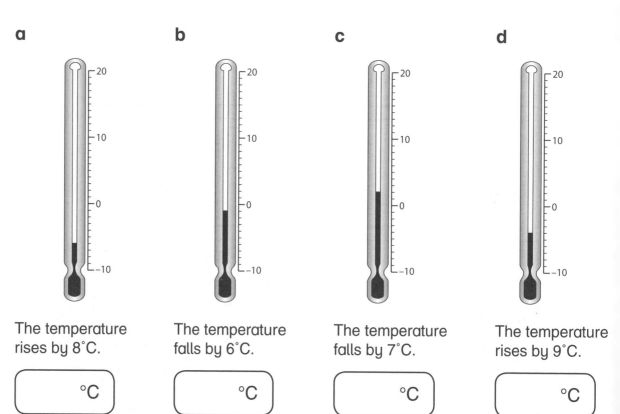

a

The temperature rises by 8°C.

°C

b

The temperature falls by 6°C.

°C

c

The temperature falls by 7°C.

°C

d

The temperature rises by 9°C.

°C

1 Write the value of each number shown by the place-value cards.

1857 → **1 8 5 7**   1000 + 800 + 50 + 7

a **3 7 9 3**   ( ) + ( ) + ( ) + ( )

b **5 7 9 3**   ( ) + ( ) + ( ) + ( )

c **5 9 9 3**   ( ) + ( ) + ( ) + ( )

d **5 9 7 3**   ( ) + ( ) + ( ) + ( )

e **5 9 7 1**   ( ) + ( ) + ( ) + ( )

f **3 9 7 1**   ( ) + ( ) + ( ) + ( )

g **3 9 5 1**   ( ) + ( ) + ( ) + ( )

h **3 7 5 1**   ( ) + ( ) + ( ) + ( )

i Draw a circle around the largest number.

j Put a star next to the smallest number.

2 Write the missing < or > signs for each pair of numbers.

a 502 ⟩ > ⟨ 205   **d** 3675 ⟩ > ⟨ 3576

b 589 ⟩ < ⟨ 598   **e** 5150 ⟩ < ⟨ 5501

c 872 ⟩ > ⟨ 871   **f** 9014 ⟩ < ⟨ 9140

 3 Write the missing symbols in each number chain.

a 971 > 917 < 1700 ⟨ ⟩ 1007 ⟨ ⟩ 1070 ⟨ ⟩ 1017

b 5412 > 5402 > 5421 ⟨ ⟩ 5461 ⟨ ⟩ 4511 ⟨ ⟩ 4155

c 8568 < 8606 < 8665 ⟨ ⟩ 8668 ⟨ ⟩ 8865 ⟨ ⟩ 5865

d 3970 < 3035 > 2978 ⟨ ⟩ 8393 ⟨ ⟩ 1638 ⟨ ⟩ 5693

 4

a Round these to the nearest 10.

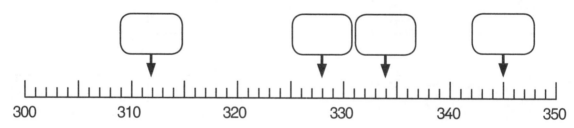

b Round these to the nearest 100.

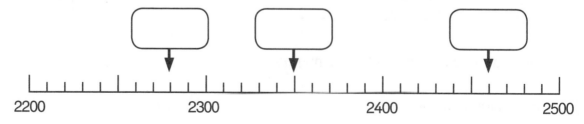

c   Round these to the nearest 1000.

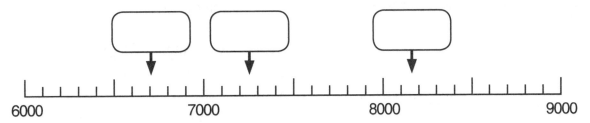

  Use the numbers on the grid to answer these.

1345	1622	1185
1179	1361	1634
1329	1614	1155
1293	1706	1162

a   To the nearest 10, which numbers round to:

1350

1620

1160

1180

b   To the nearest 100, which numbers round to:

1200

1300

1700

1400

1600

c   To the nearest 1000, which numbers round to:

1000

2000

6   This table shows some of the heaviest land mammals in the world.

Mammal	Length (cm)	Mass (kg)
African elephant	728	6945
American bison	386	1044
Arabian camel	354	687
giraffe	579	1585
gorilla	198	218
hippopotamus	403	2476
moose	291	543
polar bear	256	595
Siberian tiger	325	284
white rhinoceros	421	3606

Compare the 2 lists. Are the longer mammals always heavier than the shorter ones?

a   Which animal is heavier than the giraffe, but lighter than the white rhinoceros?

b   Which animals are longer than the moose, but shorter than the hippopotamus?

c   Choose a length from the table of animals to complete these:

[ ] > 470   [ ] < 320   585 > [ ]   291 < [ ]

d   Choose a mass from the table of animals to complete these:

2480 < [ ] < 4100   6090 > [ ] > 3360

e   Write the mammals in order of length. Start with the longest.

f   Write the mammals in order of mass. Start with the heaviest.

7 Write the halfway numbers for each number line.

a

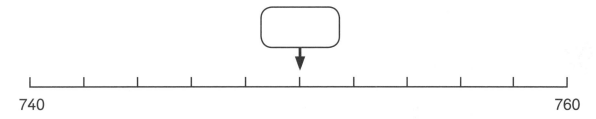

740   760

b

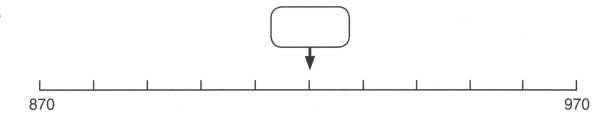

870   970

c

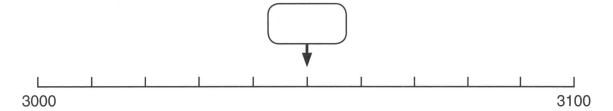

3000   3100

d

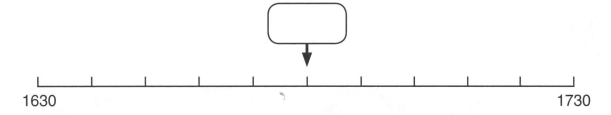

1630   1730

e

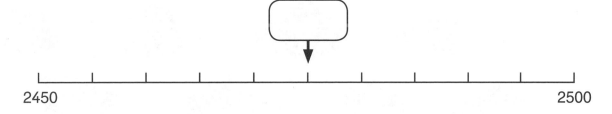

2450   2500

f

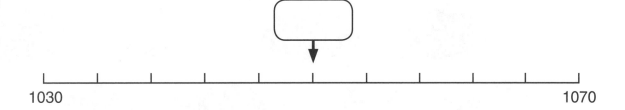

1030   1070

1 Complete this grid.

I	II		IV	V	VI				
1	2	3		5		7	8	9	10

		XII		XV		XVII		XIX	
11	12	13	14		16	17	18		20

	XL			LXX		XC			
30		50			80		100	110	120

2 Join the matching numbers and Roman numerals.

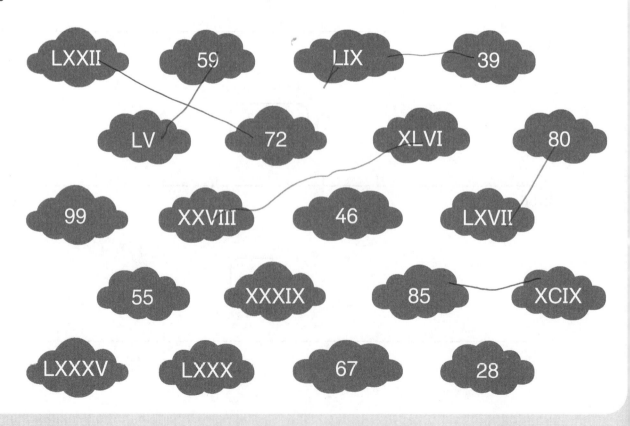

3 Write these Roman numerals as numbers.

a XXII ( )   c LXI ( )   e LXXIV ( )

b XXXV ( )   d LIX ( )   f LXXXVII ( )

4 Write these numbers as Roman numerals.

a 26 ( )   c 53 ( )   e 75 ( )

b 90 ( )   d 18 ( )   f 44 ( )

5 Draw the times on each clock face.

a

9:25

c

8:15

e

1:37

b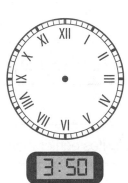

3:50

d

7:48

f

11:06

Applying addition and subtraction

6a Using mental and written methods to solve problems

1 Write these times as 24-hour clock times.

a  ☐:☐
 ☐:☐

d 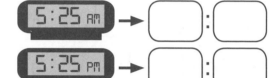 ☐:☐
 ☐:☐

b 8:55 AM → ☐:☐
8:55 PM → ☐:☐

e 11:06 AM → ☐:☐
11:06 PM → ☐:☐

c 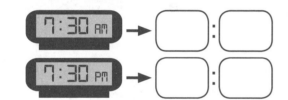 ☐:☐
☐:☐

f 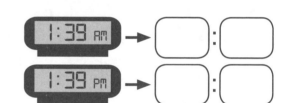 ☐:☐
☐:☐

2 Write the time that is:

a 40 minutes later than 4:25 p.m.

e 35 minutes earlier than 11:15 a.m.

b 25 minutes later than 8:50 a.m.

f 50 minutes earlier than 9:40 p.m.

c 1 hour 10 minutes later than 7:45 p.m.

g 1 hour 15 minutes earlier than 1:20 p.m.

d 4 hours 5 minutes later than 2:47 p.m.

h 2 hours 30 minutes earlier than 3:25 p.m.

3 Write the time that is:

a 20 minutes later than 12:55

e 55 minutes earlier than 11:40

b 30 minutes later than 08:14

f 45 minutes earlier than 07:05

c 1 hour 55 minutes later than 15:30

g 1 hour 30 minutes earlier than 10:50

d 2 hours 10 minutes later than 18:23

h 2 hours 10 minutes earlier than 19:48

4 Look at the map showing the length of time a bus takes between each stop.

Work out the time the bus will be at each stop and complete this bus timetable.

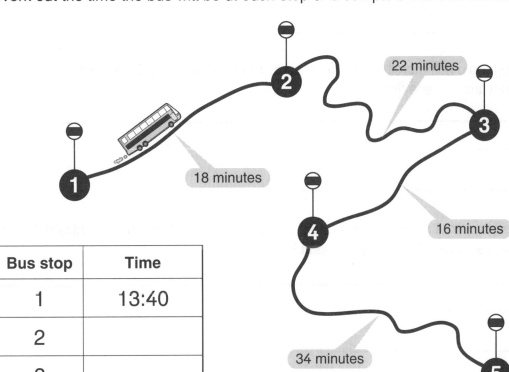

Bus stop	Time
1	13:40
2	
3	
4	
5	
6	

5 Use the number lines to help answer each problem.

a It takes Freddie 35 minutes to walk to school. If he arrives at 8:55 a.m. at what time does he leave home?

b A lorry driver travels from 9:55 a.m. until 11:40 a.m. to deliver bricks. How long did his journey take?

c A market stall opens at 6:15 a.m. and closes at 12:05 p.m.. How long is the stall open for?

d Kay ran a half marathon and finished in 1 hour 35 minutes. If the race started at 10:15, what time did she finish?

e A flight from London to Paris takes 1 hour 15 minutes. The 15:30 flight is delayed by 40 minutes. What time will it now land in Paris?

f Sam goes to bed at 20:50 p.m. and sleeps for 9 hours 25 minutes. What time does he wake up?

6 Complete these two charts.

a

Length in m and cm	Length in cm
9 m 22 cm	922 cm
1 m 50 cm	cm
m cm	280 cm
3 m 25 cm	cm
m cm	705 cm
6 m 9 cm	cm

b

Length in km and m	Length in m
9 km 700 m	9700 m
8 km 131 m	m
km m	7620 m
1 km 8 m	m
6 km 50 m	m
km m	3045 m

 7 Use a bar model to represent each of these and then calculate the answers.

Show your mental or written methods.

a

681 m + 320 m =

c
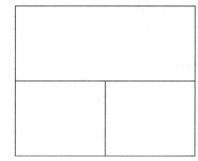
2850 m − 645 m =

b
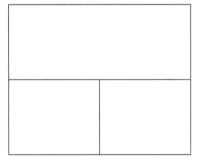
4893 m − 1039 m =

d
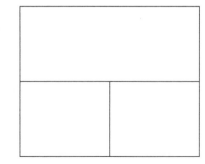
4718 m + 3893 m =

8 A cyclist goes on some rides from Sea Point to different places.

What is the total distance for each route?

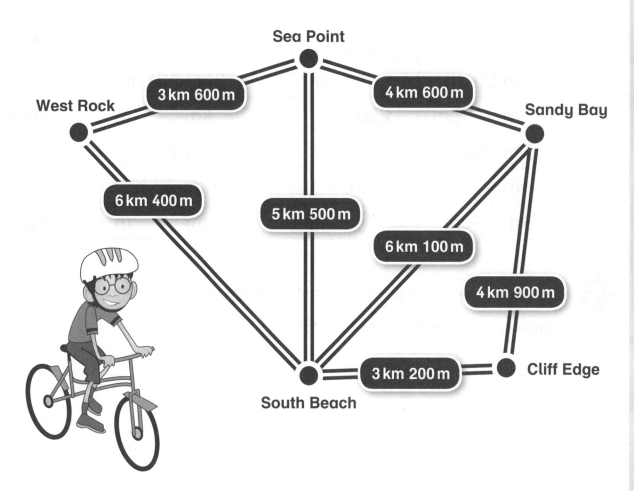

a Sea Point ➔ West Rock ➔ South Beach

b West Rock ➔ South Beach ➔ Sea Point

c Sea Point ➔ Sandy Bay ➔ South Beach ➔ Sea Point

d Sea Point ➔ South Beach ➔ Cliff Edge ➔ Sandy Bay ➔ Sea Point

6b Bar models and bar charts

1 Calculate the unknown value for each of these. Show your working.

a

3400	
2100	

c

4500		
1050		680

b

740	290

d

890	640
	750

2 Mr Khan is a dentist. This graph shows the number of patients who visited him each month for 6 months.

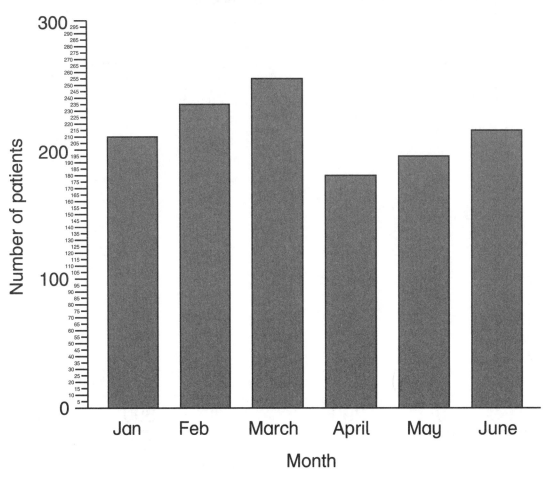

a How many patients visited Mr Khan in May?

b In which month was Mr Khan visited by 210 people?

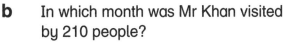

c In which month did the most patients visit Mr Khan?

d How many fewer patients visited him in April than in June?

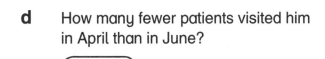

e How many more patients visited him in March than in February?

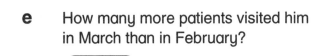

f How many people visited Mr Khan altogether during these 6 months?

3 Sophie's school is collecting cans for recycling.

For 2 weeks they count up the cans collected. This graph shows the results.

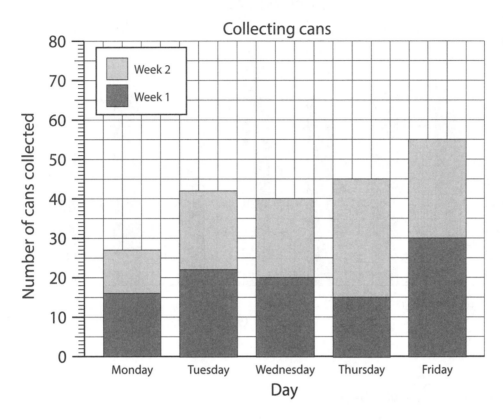

a How many cans were collected on Monday of Week 1?

b How many cans were collected on Friday of Week 2?

c How many cans were collected in total over both weeks on Tuesday?

d How many more cans were collected on Thursday of Week 2 than Thursday of Week 1?

e On which day were the same numbers of cans collected for Week 1 and 2?

f On which day were the most cans collected in Week 1?

g On which day were the fewest cans collected in Week 2?

h Complete the graph for Week 3 using these results.

Mon	Tues	Wed	Thur	Fri
18	24	31	17	32

4   This graph shows the speeds of some of the fastest land animals.

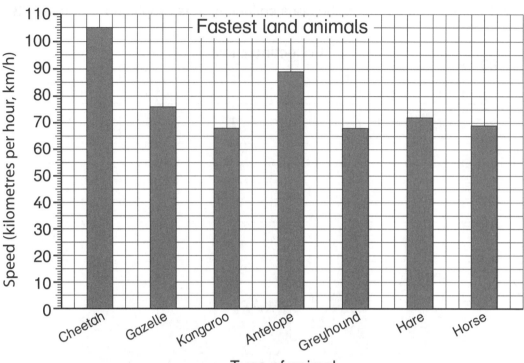

Type of animal

Use the graph to answer these.

a   At what speed can a gazelle run?

[　　　　km/h　]

b   Which animal runs at 72 km/h?

[　　　　　　　　　]

c   Which two animals run at the same speed?

[　　　　　　　　　]

d   Which is the fastest animal?

[　　　　　　　　　]

e   Which is fastest, a greyhound or a hare?

[　　　　　　　　　]

f   What is the speed of the second fastest animal?

[　　　　km/h　]

g   Which animal is exactly 20 km/h slower than an antelope?

[　　　　　　　　　]

h   How much faster does a cheetah run than the second fastest animal?

[　　　　km/h　]

Investigate the speed of the fastest sea creatures.

Here are some to start you off.

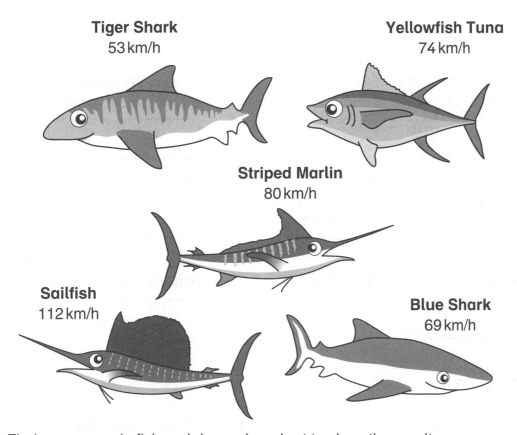

Tiger Shark
53 km/h

Yellowfish Tuna
74 km/h

Striped Marlin
80 km/h

Sailfish
112 km/h

Blue Shark
69 km/h

Find more speedy fish and draw a bar chart to show the results.

6c Solving problems

⭐ 1 Answer these.

a How much heavier is 5623 g than 4920 g?

[g]

b What is 290 seconds added to 2 minutes 15 seconds?

[minutes] [seconds]

c What is 5925 ml added to 7190 ml?

[ml]

d What is the difference between 3 km 800 m and 5 km 200 m?

[km] [m]

e How much longer is 1285 m than 893 m?

[m]

f What is the total weight of 5290 g and 8560 g?

[g]

⭐ 2 Answer these.

a A library has 2845 books. 1039 of the books are reference books and the rest are fiction. 87 of the reference books and 276 of the fiction books are out on loan. How many books are there left in the library?

[   ]

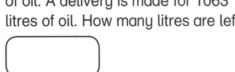

b A shop has 1045 apples. It sells 768 apples in the morning and 237 apples in the afternoon. How many apples does it have left at the end of the day?

[   ]

c An oil tanker lorry contains 2683 litres of oil. A delivery is made for 1063 litres of oil. How many litres are left?

[   ]

d A farmer needs 8450 kg of animal feed a week to feed his cattle. After 5 days, he has 2465 kg left. How much feed has the farmer used in the first 5 days?

[kg]

e A rabbit hutch has 2 sides each 3625 cm, and the other 2 sides each 1436 cm. Wire is used round the sides. What is the total length of wire needed?

[cm]

f A father and his son weigh a total of 87 kg. If the father weighs 68 kg 295 g, what is the mass of the son?

[kg] [g]

3

Look at these items and answer the questions.

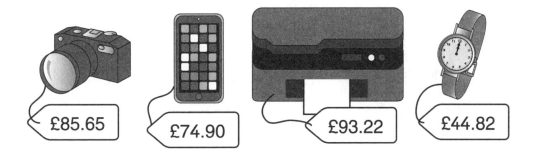

£85.65   £74.90   £93.22   £44.82

a What is the difference in price between the camera and the watch?

£

b How much more is it to buy a printer than a phone?

£

c If the watch is bought with a £50 note, how much change will be given?

£

d How much less does it cost to buy a camera than a printer?

£

e Nadia has two £20 notes. How much more does she need to buy the camera?

£

4

Mr Lucas has 3 sheep, A, B and C.
Each has a different mass that is an exact number of kilograms.

A   B   C

Sheep A and B weigh a total of 77 kg.
Sheep B and C weigh a total of 72 kg.
Sheep A and C weigh a total of 65 kg.

What is the mass of each sheep?

A weighs [   ] kg   B weighs [   ] kg   C weighs [   ] kg

Unit 7 Fractions and decimals

7a Families of fractions

1 Write the fraction shaded for each of these as mixed numbers and improper fractions.

a

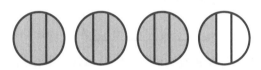

c

b

d

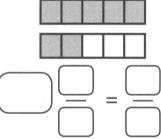

2 Write the fraction each arrow points to, as an improper fraction and as a mixed number.

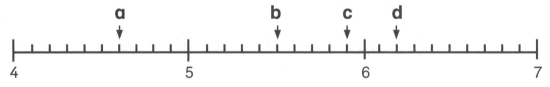

a

c

b

d

3 Write the equivalent fractions shown on each fraction bar.

a

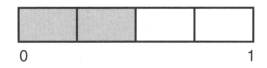

0   1

$\dfrac{2}{\Box} = \dfrac{1}{\Box}$

b

0   1

$\dfrac{2}{\Box} = \dfrac{1}{\Box}$

c

0   1

$\dfrac{3}{\Box} = \dfrac{1}{\Box}$

d

0   1

$\dfrac{2}{\Box} = \dfrac{1}{\Box}$

e

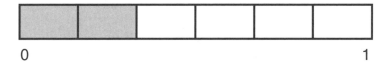

0   1

$\dfrac{4}{\Box} = \dfrac{1}{\Box}$

f

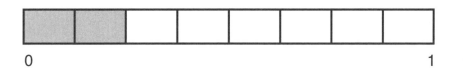

0   1

$\dfrac{4}{\Box} = \dfrac{2}{\Box}$

g

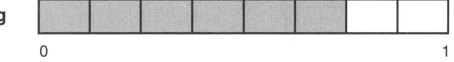

0   1

$\dfrac{6}{\Box} = \dfrac{3}{\Box}$

4 Complete these equivalent fraction chains.

a $\dfrac{1}{2} = \dfrac{2}{\boxed{}} = \dfrac{\boxed{}}{6} = \dfrac{4}{\boxed{}} = \dfrac{\boxed{}}{\boxed{}} = \dfrac{\boxed{}}{\boxed{}}$

b $\dfrac{1}{3} = \dfrac{\boxed{}}{6} = \dfrac{3}{\boxed{}} = \dfrac{\boxed{}}{12} = \dfrac{\boxed{}}{\boxed{}} = \dfrac{\boxed{}}{\boxed{}}$

c $\dfrac{1}{4} = \dfrac{2}{\boxed{}} = \dfrac{\boxed{}}{12} = \dfrac{4}{\boxed{}} = \dfrac{\boxed{}}{\boxed{}} = \dfrac{\boxed{}}{\boxed{}}$

d $\dfrac{1}{6} = \dfrac{\boxed{}}{12} = \dfrac{3}{\boxed{}} = \dfrac{\boxed{}}{24} = \dfrac{\boxed{}}{\boxed{}} = \dfrac{\boxed{}}{\boxed{}}$

e $\dfrac{1}{12} = \dfrac{2}{\boxed{}} = \dfrac{\boxed{}}{36} = \dfrac{4}{\boxed{}} = \dfrac{\boxed{}}{\boxed{}} = \dfrac{\boxed{}}{\boxed{}}$

 5

YOU WILL NEED:
- **colouring pencils**

Colour each shape to help you add these fractions. Complete each answer.

a

$\dfrac{2}{5} + \dfrac{2}{5} = \dfrac{\boxed{}}{5}$

b

$\dfrac{4}{10} + \dfrac{3}{10} = \dfrac{\boxed{}}{10}$

c

$\dfrac{3}{8} + \dfrac{2}{8} = \dfrac{\boxed{}}{8}$

6 Answer these.

a $\dfrac{2}{7} + \dfrac{3}{7} = \dfrac{\boxed{}}{\boxed{}}$

 $\dfrac{2}{8} + \dfrac{3}{8} = \dfrac{\boxed{}}{\boxed{}}$

 $\dfrac{2}{9} + \dfrac{3}{9} = \dfrac{\boxed{}}{\boxed{}}$

c $\dfrac{1}{7} + \dfrac{2}{7} = \dfrac{\boxed{}}{\boxed{}}$

 $\dfrac{3}{7} + \dfrac{4}{7} = \dfrac{\boxed{}}{\boxed{}}$

 $\dfrac{5}{7} + \dfrac{6}{7} = \dfrac{\boxed{}}{\boxed{}}$

b $\dfrac{5}{10} - \dfrac{3}{10} = \dfrac{\boxed{}}{\boxed{}}$

 $\dfrac{5}{8} - \dfrac{3}{8} = \dfrac{\boxed{}}{\boxed{}}$

 $\dfrac{5}{6} - \dfrac{3}{6} = \dfrac{\boxed{}}{\boxed{}}$

d $\dfrac{7}{10} - \dfrac{4}{10} = \dfrac{\boxed{}}{\boxed{}}$

 $\dfrac{6}{10} - \dfrac{3}{10} = \dfrac{\boxed{}}{\boxed{}}$

 $\dfrac{5}{10} - \dfrac{2}{10} = \dfrac{\boxed{}}{\boxed{}}$

 7 Complete the fractions, writing in these missing digits:

2   3   4   5   6   7

 $\dfrac{3}{4} - \dfrac{1}{\boxed{}} = \dfrac{1}{4}$

 $\dfrac{3}{\boxed{}} + \dfrac{1}{5} = \dfrac{\boxed{}}{5}$

 $\dfrac{1}{10} + \dfrac{\boxed{}}{10} = \dfrac{4}{5}$

 $\dfrac{5}{\boxed{}} - \dfrac{1}{6} = \dfrac{2}{\boxed{}}$

8   Answer these problems.

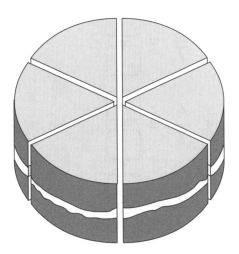

a   A cake is divided into 6 equal pieces. $\frac{1}{3}$ of the cake is eaten and then $\frac{1}{2}$ of the pieces that are left are eaten. How many pieces of cake are left?

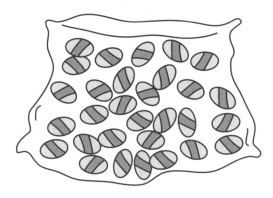

b   A bag of sweets is shared out between 3 brothers. Daniel has $\frac{3}{10}$ of them and Adam has $\frac{1}{10}$ of the sweets. What fraction of the sweets does Matt have?

c   If there are 30 sweets altogether, how many sweets does each brother get?

Daniel

Adam

Matt

1 Write both the common fraction and decimal fraction for each arrow.

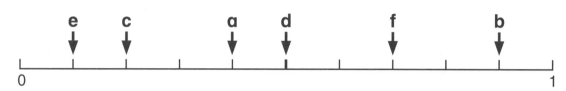

a 　　c 　　e

b 　　d 　　f

2 Look at the shaded areas. Write the fraction and decimal for each.

a 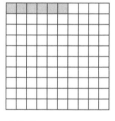　　c 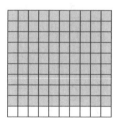　　e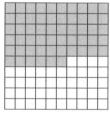

b 　　d 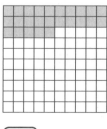　　f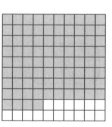

3 Write these as fractions.

a   0.5 $\dfrac{\boxed{}}{\boxed{}}$ d   0.05 $\dfrac{\boxed{}}{\boxed{}}$ g   26.2 $\boxed{}\dfrac{\boxed{}}{\boxed{}}$

b   0.3 $\dfrac{\boxed{}}{\boxed{}}$ e   0.89 $\dfrac{\boxed{}}{\boxed{}}$ h   88.6 $\boxed{}\dfrac{\boxed{}}{\boxed{}}$

c   0.03 $\dfrac{\boxed{}}{\boxed{}}$ f   0.75 $\dfrac{\boxed{}}{\boxed{}}$ i   4.33 $\boxed{}\dfrac{\boxed{}}{\boxed{}}$

 4 Write these as decimals.

a $\dfrac{4}{10}$ $\boxed{}$ f $\dfrac{65}{100}$ $\boxed{}$

b $\dfrac{1}{5}$ $\boxed{}$ g $2\dfrac{4}{5}$ $\boxed{}$

c $\dfrac{5}{100}$ $\boxed{}$ h $7\dfrac{2}{5}$ $\boxed{}$

d $\dfrac{7}{100}$ $\boxed{}$ i $4\dfrac{11}{50}$ $\boxed{}$

e $\dfrac{31}{50}$ $\boxed{}$ j $6\dfrac{3}{25}$ $\boxed{}$

5

Use a calculator to explore decimal patterns.

a Key this in to make a ×10 machine:

Repeat this, changing 1.75 to other numbers. Explain what is happening.

b Key this in to make a ÷10 machine:

Repeat, changing 65 to other numbers. Explain what is happening.

Unit 8 Methods for multiplying

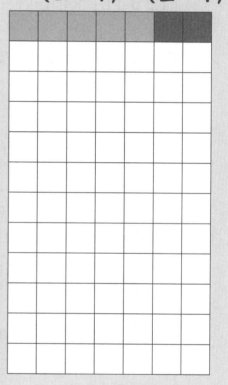

1 Complete these.

a $7 \times 1 = (5 \times 1) + (2 \times 1) = $ ☐

b $7 \times 2 = (5 \times 2) + (2 \times 2) = $ ☐

c $7 \times 3 = (5 \times 3) + (2 \times 3) = $ ☐

d $7 \times 4 = (5 \times 4) + (2 \times 4) = $ ☐

e $7 \times 5 = (5 \times 5) + (2 \times 5) = $ ☐

f $7 \times 6 = (5 \times 6) + (2 \times 6) = $ ☐

g $7 \times 7 = (5 \times 7) + (2 \times 7) = $ ☐

h $7 \times 8 = (5 \times 8) + (2 \times 8) = $ ☐

i $7 \times 9 = (5 \times 9) + (2 \times 9) = $ ☐

j $7 \times 10 = (5 \times 10) + (2 \times 10) = $ ☐

k $7 \times 11 = (5 \times 11) + (2 \times 11) = $ ☐

l $7 \times 12 = (5 \times 12) + (2 \times 12) = $ ☐

2 Complete these.

A number line from 0 to 140, marked in intervals of 10.

0   10   20   30   40   50   60   70   80   90   100   110   120   130   140

a $11 \times 1 = (10 \times 1) + 1 = \boxed{}$

b $11 \times 2 = (10 \times 2) + 2 = \boxed{}$

c $11 \times 3 = (10 \times 3) + 3 = \boxed{}$

d $11 \times 4 = (10 \times 4) + 4 = \boxed{}$

e $11 \times 5 = (10 \times 5) + 5 = \boxed{}$

f $11 \times 6 = (10 \times 6) + 6 = \boxed{}$

g $11 \times 7 = (10 \times 7) + 7 = \boxed{}$

h $11 \times 8 = (10 \times 8) + 8 = \boxed{}$

i $11 \times 9 = (10 \times 9) + 9 = \boxed{}$

j $11 \times 10 = (10 \times 10) + 10 = \boxed{}$

k $11 \times 11 = (10 \times 11) + 11 = \boxed{}$

l $11 \times 12 = (10 \times 12) + 12 = \boxed{}$

3 Continue the patterns.

a

7   14   21

b

84   77   70

c

11   22   33

d

132   121   110

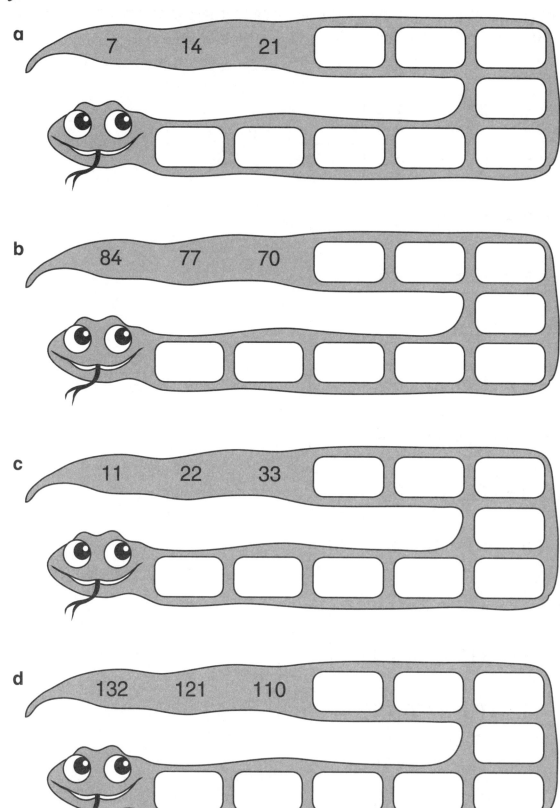

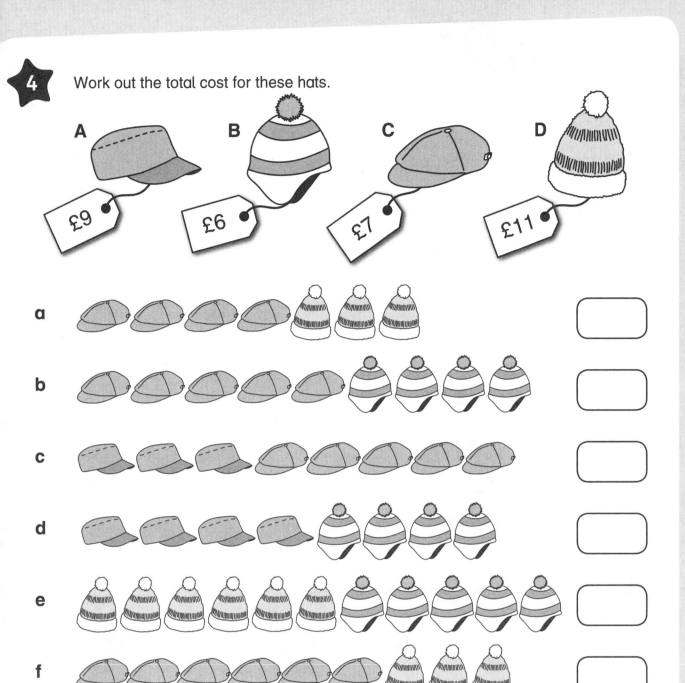

4 Work out the total cost for these hats.

A £9   B £6   C £7   D £11

a

b

c

d

e

f

 6 Complete these.

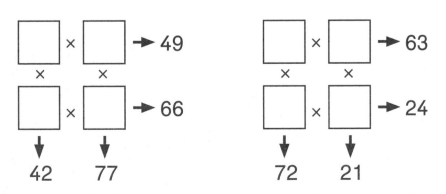

$\square \times \square \rightarrow 49$
$\times \quad \times$
$\square \times \square \rightarrow 66$
$\downarrow \qquad \downarrow$
42   77

$\square \times \square \rightarrow 63$
$\times \quad \times$
$\square \times \square \rightarrow 24$
$\downarrow \qquad \downarrow$
72   21

8b Three at once

1 Answer these.

a $3 \times 2 \times 4 = \boxed{}$

$2 \times 4 \times 3 = \boxed{}$

$4 \times 3 \times 2 = \boxed{}$

c $7 \times 11 \times 10 = \boxed{}$

$11 \times 10 \times 7 = \boxed{}$

$10 \times 7 \times 11 = \boxed{}$

b $6 \times 5 \times 2 = \boxed{}$

$5 \times 2 \times 6 = \boxed{}$

$2 \times 6 \times 5 = \boxed{}$

d $5 \times 4 \times 8 = \boxed{}$

$8 \times 5 \times 4 = \boxed{}$

$4 \times 8 \times 5 = \boxed{}$

What do you notice about the answers for each?

2 Write the missing numbers in each of these.

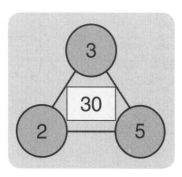

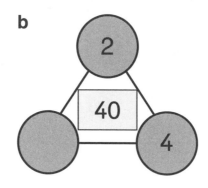

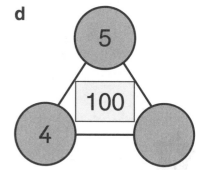

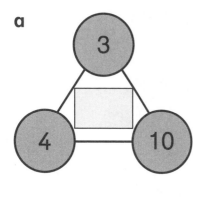

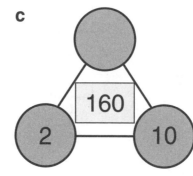

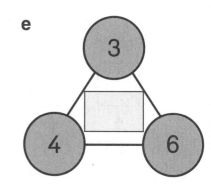

3 These show different sized sheets of stamps.

Calculate the total number of stamps for each sheet.

a

2 sheets ➡ total number of stamps ☐

5 sheets ➡ total number of stamps ☐

7 sheets ➡ total number of stamps ☐

12 sheets ➡ total number of stamps ☐

b

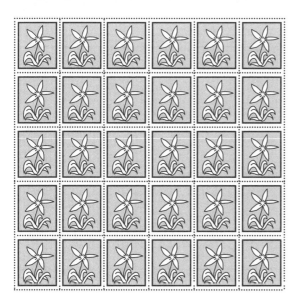

2 sheets ➡ total number of stamps ☐

5 sheets ➡ total number of stamps ☐

7 sheets ➡ total number of stamps ☐

12 sheets ➡ total number of stamps ☐

4 A football team has 2 kits of tops, shorts and socks. One kit is all red and the other kit is all yellow.

All the players wear the same kit, but sometimes they mix the socks, shorts and tops to make different kits, such as red socks, red shorts and a yellow top.

a How many different combinations of kit are there by mixing them in different ways? Show your working.

b The team adds a third black kit.
How many different combinations of red, yellow and black kits do they now have?

1 Answer these.

a $71 \times 5 \rightarrow$ $70 \times 5 = \boxed{}$
$1 \times 5 = \boxed{}$ $+$
___
$71 \times 5 = \boxed{}$

c $26 \times 7 \rightarrow$ $20 \times 7 = \boxed{}$
$6 \times 7 = \boxed{}$ $+$
___
$26 \times 7 = \boxed{}$

b $59 \times 4 \rightarrow$ $50 \times 4 = \boxed{}$
$9 \times 4 = \boxed{}$ $+$
___
$59 \times 4 = \boxed{}$

d $48 \times 6 \rightarrow$ $40 \times 6 = \boxed{}$
$8 \times 6 = \boxed{}$ $+$
___
$48 \times 6 = \boxed{}$

2 Complete these.

a $74 \times 3 = \boxed{}$

$\times$	70	4
3			$\rightarrow$

c $29 \times 7 = \boxed{}$

$\times$	20	9
7			$\rightarrow$

b $83 \times 5 = \boxed{}$

$\times$	80	3
5			$\rightarrow$

d $57 \times 9 = \boxed{}$

$\times$	50	7
9			$\rightarrow$

3 Answer these.

a
```
    1 9
×     4
```

c
```
    8 5
×     6
```

e
```
    9 2
×     7
```

b
```
    3 6
×     5
```

d
```
    6 7
×     3
```

f
```
    6 3
×     8
```

4 Answer these.

Choose a method for working out each answer.

a $96 \times 5 =$

c $54 \times 9 =$

b $47 \times 3 =$

d $73 \times 8 =$

5 Sam owns 5 lorries. Each lorry has a maximum number of boxes it can carry.

a Complete this chart.

Lorry	Maximum number of boxes			
	1 journey	**2 journeys**	**5 journeys**	**7 journeys**
A	28	56		
B	52			
C	45		225	
D	36			
E	64	128		

b Lorry A and Lorry B both make 5 journeys. How many boxes do they carry in total?

c Lorry C and Lorry D both make 7 journeys.
How many more boxes does Lorry C carry?

6 Write the total cost of these sports items.

 £17

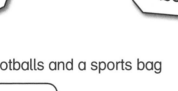 £68

£28

£46

a 3 footballs and a sports bag

c 5 pairs of trainers and 2 footballs

b 4 tennis rackets and a pair of trainers

d 3 sports bags and 2 tennis rackets

1 Write the value of the unknown number, in the shaded box.

a

7			

e

36

b

7						

f

36

c

7			

g

36

d

7								

h

36

What do you notice?

2 What number is...

a 5 times larger than 6?

☐

e 6 times smaller than 42?

☐

b 6 times larger than 5?

☐

f 3 times smaller than 21?

☐

c 3 times larger than 8?

☐

g 8 times smaller than 48?

☐

d 8 times larger than 3?

☐

h 4 times smaller than 24?

☐

What do you notice?

3 Solve these problems.

a An aeroplane has 40 rows of seats and 7 seats in each row. What is the maximum number of passengers that could sit on this aeroplane?

☐

b The cost of a return flight is £300 per person.
What will be the total cost for a family of 6 to travel?

☐

c 7 people on the flight pay £60 each for extra leg room.
How much in total is paid for extra leg room?

☐

d The total cost for theme park tickets for a group of 7 adults is £210.
What is the cost of one ticket?

☐

e There are 100 seats on a roller coaster and each carriage has 4 seats.
How many carriages are there on this roller coaster?

☐

f The ghost train leaves every 5 minutes.
How many times does the ghost train leave in 1 hour?

☐

4 Read this recipe.

Fabulous Flapjacks

• •

240 g oats   Makes 12 pieces

120 g butter   Oven setting: 180˚C/350˚F

60 g brown sugar

40 g golden syrup

1. Grease a baking tin (approx 20 × 30 cm).

2. Put the butter, sugar and syrup in a saucepan and melt over a very low heat.

3. Take the pan off the heat and add the oats, stirring well with a wooden spoon.

4. Pour the mixture into the tin and press down.

5. Bake for 20 minutes.

6. Cut the flapjacks into 12 rectangular pieces. Leave in the tin until cool.

This recipe makes 12 pieces of flapjack. Write how much of each ingredient you would need to make the following, with the same size pieces:

a 6 pieces of flapjack:

[ ] g oats   [ ] g brown sugar

[ ] g butter   [ ] g golden syrup

c 24 pieces of flapjack:

[ ] g oats   [ ] g brown sugar

[ ] g butter   [ ] g golden syrup

b 3 pieces of flapjack:

[ ] g oats   [ ] g brown sugar

[ ] g butter   [ ] g golden syrup

d 18 pieces of flapjack:

[ ] g oats   [ ] g brown sugar

[ ] g butter   [ ] g golden syrup

9a Trapeziums and kites

1 Put a star next to the odd shape out in each set. Name the odd one out.

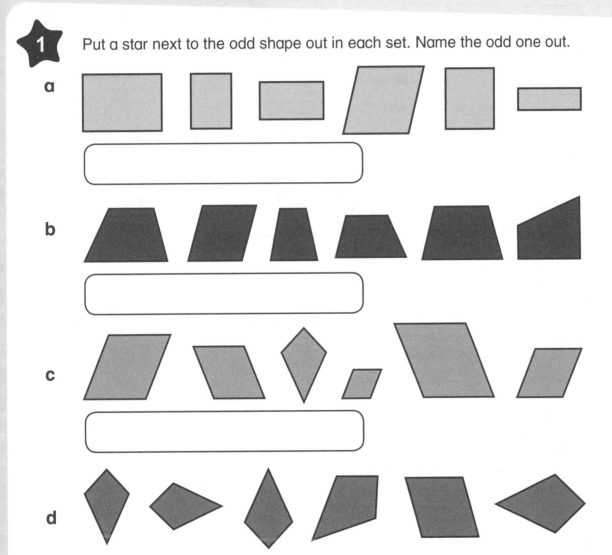

a

b

c

d

2 Look at these quadrilaterals. Draw lines of symmetry on any symmetrical shape.

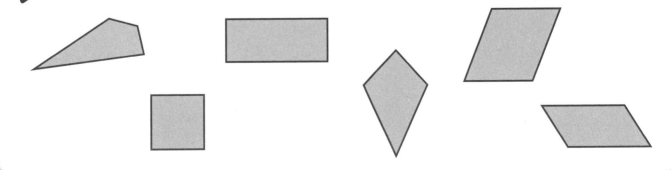

3 Look at these shapes.

Complete the chart by ticking the names.

Remember, some shapes may have more than one name.

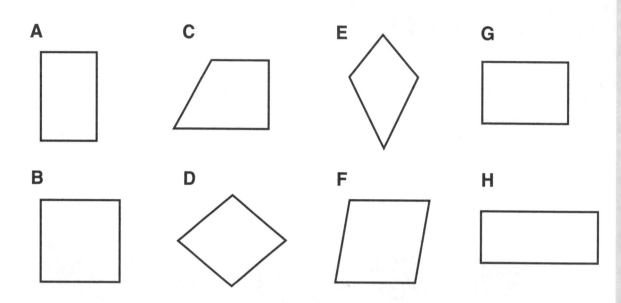

A   C   E   G

B   D   F   H

Shape	A	B	C	D	E	F	G	H
Square								
Rhombus								
Rectangle								
Parallelogram								
Trapezium								
Kite								

4 Draw each shape in its correct place on the diagram.

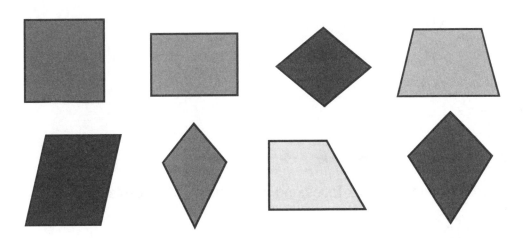

	Right angles	No right angles
Parallel lines		
No parallel lines		

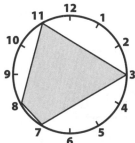

The points joined are: 11 ➡ 3 ➡ 7 ➡ 8 ➡ 11

Join the points on these clock faces and name the quadrilaterals.

a

1 ➡ 3 ➡ 5 ➡ 11 ➡ 1

b

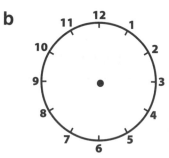

2 ➡ 4 ➡ 8 ➡ 10 ➡ 2

c

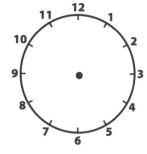

3 ➡ 6 ➡ 9 ➡ 12 ➡ 3

Explore different quadrilaterals you can draw on a clock face.

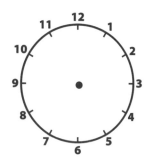

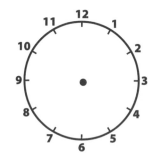

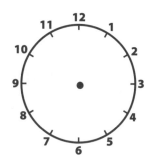

9b Coordinates and translations

1 Look at the position of each shape on this coordinates grid.

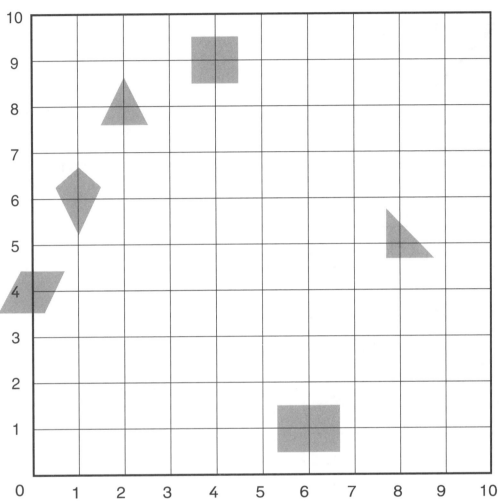

a Write the coordinates of the centre of each of these shapes:

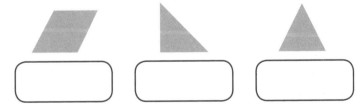

b Which shapes are at these coordinates?

(4, 9) ➡

(6, 1) ➡

(1, 6) ➡

2 Here are 2 sides of a square.

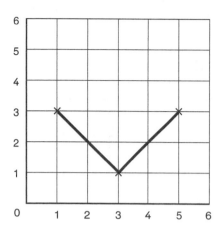

a Mark the missing coordinates for the fourth vertex and complete the square.

b What are the coordinates of the 4 vertices?

(,   ),(,   ),(,   ),(,   )

3 Plot these coordinates: A (4, 5) B (6, 3) C (4, 0) D (2, 3)

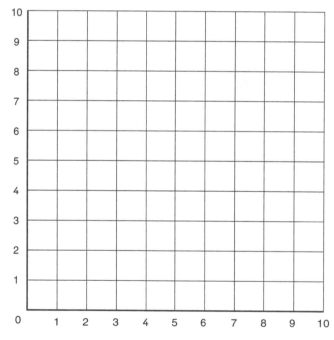

a Join the coordinates with a ruler to make a quadrilateral. The shape is a

b Translate your shape so that it is 4 squares across to the right and 2 squares up. Draw the new shape.

c What are the coordinates of the vertices of your translated shape?

(,   ),(,   ),(,   ),(,   )

4 A shape tile can be moved by translation. The shape slides without rotating or flipping over.

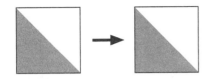

Repeat these shape tiles to design a translation pattern.

a

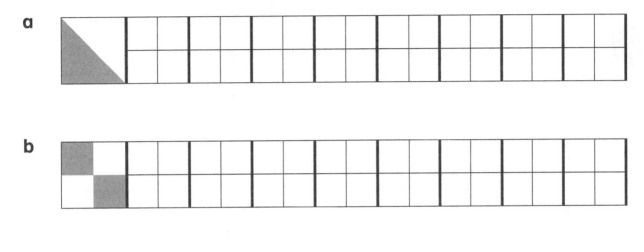

b

c

Make up your own tile and translation pattern.

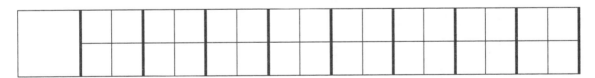

10a 25s and 1000s

1 Write in words the value of the **bold** digit.

a   3**4**43 [   ]   d   100**4** [   ]

b   **4**091 [   ]   e   **4**994 [   ]

c   3**4**59 [   ]   f   20**4**8 [   ]

2 Look at the abacus then complete the sentences.

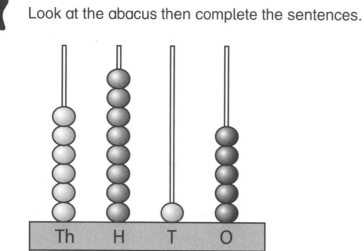

Th   H   T   O

a   10 more than 6815 is

[   ]

b   10 less than 6815 is

[   ]

c   100 more than 6815 is

[   ]

d   100 less than 6815 is

[   ]

e   1000 more than 6815 is

[   ]

f   1000 less than 6815 is

[   ]

3 Write each number.

a 1 less than 1000

[ ]

d 1000 less than 8787

[ ]

b 100 more than 4900

[ ]

e 10 less than 3100

[ ]

c 1000 more than 2999

[ ]

f 10 more than 8990

[ ]

4 Write the missing numbers in each sequence.

a 800 [ ] 900 950 1000 [ ] 1100

b 1120 [ ] 1320 1420 [ ] [ ] 1720

c 1030 2030 [ ] [ ] 5030 [ ] 7030

d 425 [ ] [ ] 500 525 [ ] 575

5 Read these scales. Write each mass in grams and kilograms.

a

(g) = (kg)

d

(g) = (kg)

b

(g) = (kg)

e

(g) = (kg)

c

(g) = (kg)

f

(g) = (kg)

6 250 is the middle number in a sequence of 7 numbers.

___ ___ ___ **250** ___ ___ ___

This is a possible sequence:

220, 230, 240, **250**, 260, 270, 280

Write three different sequences with 250 as the middle number.

 250

 250

 250

1 Write each of these in order, starting with the smallest.

a
40 m   400 cm   4 km   400 m

[ ] [ ] [ ] [ ]

b 1.8 litres   180 ml   18 litres   1080 ml

[ ] [ ] [ ] [ ]

c 3.5 km   350 m   3.05 m   350 cm

[ ] [ ] [ ] [ ]

d 1½ kg   1250 g   1050 g   1.2 kg

[ ] [ ] [ ] [ ]

e 0.6 litres   60 ml   6600 ml   6 litres

[ ] [ ] [ ] [ ]

2 Write the measures shown for each of these.

a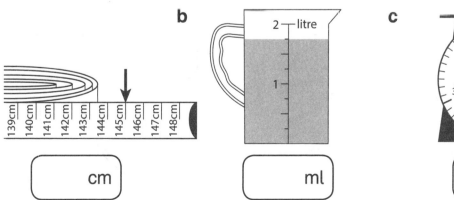

[cm]

b

[ml]

c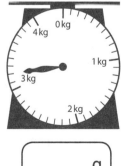

[g]

3 Write the amount of water in each jug as millilitres and litres.

a

[ml] = [litres]

d

[ml] = [litres]

b

[ml] = [litres]

e

[ml] = [litres]

c

[ml] = [litres]

f

[ml] = [litres]

4 Write the greater capacity in each pair.

a

1050 ml | 1.5 litre

c
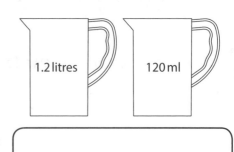

1.2 litres | 120 ml

b
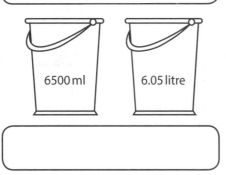

6500 ml | 6.05 litre

d

4000 ml | 0.4 litre

5 Look at this bus timetable.

	Bus A	**Bus B**	**Bus C**	**Bus D**
School	08:15	09:35	11:05	13:55
Hospital	08:35	09:50	11:30	14:15
Market	08:45	10:00	11:40	14:35
Town centre	09:10	10:30	12:05	14:45

a Which is the fastest bus from the school to the town centre?

c Which bus takes 35 minutes to travel from the school to the market?

b Which is the slowest bus from the hospital to the town centre?

d How many minutes are there between Bus C and Bus D leaving the school?

minutes

 6 Write the total amount of liquid in this fruit punch.

Fruit Punch

• • • • • • • • • • • • • •

1.2 litres orange juice

300 ml mango juice

250 ml apple juice

0.25 litres coconut milk

a Total: litres

b How many 250 ml glasses can be filled?

glasses

11a Solving problems using written methods

1 Use the number lines to help work out the change from £10 for each of these.

a £4.85

£4.85 £5.00   £10.00

[ ] + [ ] = [ ] change

b £6.56

£6.56 £6.60   £7.00   £10.00

[ ] + [ ] + [ ] = [ ] change

c £2.34

[number line]

£2.34 £2.40   £3.00   £10.00

[ ] + [ ] + [ ] = [ ] change

d £7.71

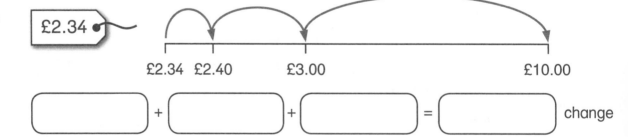

£7.71 £7.80   £8.00   £10.00

[ ] + [ ] + [ ] = [ ] change

2   Look at this café menu to answer these.

café menu

● ● ● ● ● ● ● ● ● ● ● ● ● ● ● ● ● ● ●

Fish and chips . . .   £6.95

Pie and mash £5.15

Chicken salad. . . .   £5.46

Ham and eggs £4.12

Cheese omelette. . .   £4.85

Veg stir fry £6.05

a   What are the fewest number of coins you would need to buy the cheese omelette?

b   What are the fewest number of coins you would have as change from £10 for the fish and chips?

c   Sam paid for a chicken salad with a £5 note and 5 coins. He only used 2 different coins. Which coins were they?

d   Vic also had a chicken salad and paid with a £5 note. She also only had 2 different types of coin. However, she used 7 coins. Which coins were they?

e   Which 2 items total exactly £10?

3 Complete these.

Remember to estimate first, then check your answer using the inverse.

a   £ 47.09
      + £ 28.34
      _____

c   £ 38.69
      + £ 45.72
      _____

b   £ 42.55
      + £ 54.95
      _____

d   £ 54.83
      + £ 39.59
      _____

4 Complete these.

a   £ 55.90
      −   £ 27.32
      _____

c   £ 99.05
      − £ 68.56
      _____

b   £ 71.23
      − £ 33.49
      _____

d   £ 60.40
      − £ 39.99
      _____

5 This chart shows how much money a market stall made over 1 week.

Look at the chart and answer these questions.

Sunday	Monday	Tuesday	Wednesday	Thursday	Friday	Saturday
£38.44	£94.75	£83.92	£51.80	£47.64	£92.55	£87.58

a How much money was taken in total on Wednesday and Thursday?

c How much money was made on the first 3 days of the week?

b How much more money was made on Saturday than on Sunday?

d Which 2 days had a difference of £2.20?

6 Look at these prices and answer the questions.

£19.52   £45.59   £20.81   £25.22   £37.68

a What is the largest total that can be made by totalling 2 of these prices?

c What is the total of the lowest price and the highest price?

b What is the smallest total that can be made by totalling 2 of these prices?

d Which 2 prices when bought together would give a total price of £44.74?

1 Answer these.

a 35 + 8 = ☐

350 + 80 = ☐

3500 + 800 = ☐

c 79 – 5 = ☐

790 – 50 = ☐

7900 – 500 = ☐

b 24 + 7 = ☐

240 + 70 = ☐

2400 + 700 = ☐

d 94 – 6 = ☐

940 – 60 = ☐

9400 – 600 = ☐

2 Write the missing numbers on these addition grids.

+	700	3900	
600			
4200			
1800			6800

+	2100	5700	
		10 200	
900			5000
	4700		

3 These are pyramid sums for 10 000.

The number above is the total of the 2 numbers below.

a
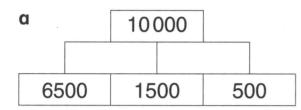

c
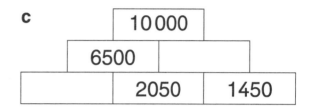

b
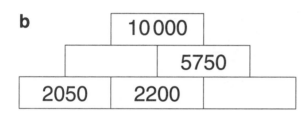

d
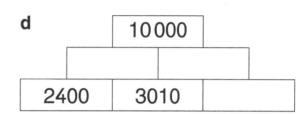

Make up your own 10 000 pyramid for others to try.

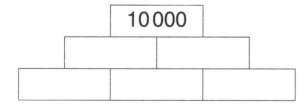

4 Write the numbers going in and out of each function machine.

a

600

900

[ ]

[ ]

1800

IN ×2 +300 OUT

[ ]

[ ]

2700

3300

[ ]

b

3500

4500

[ ]

[ ]

7500

IN +1200 −600 OUT

[ ]

[ ]

6100

7100

[ ]

5 Ali plays a computer game each day. He is trying to reach a total of 20 000 points to go on to the next level.

These are his points for the first three days.

Day	Points
Monday	3800
Tuesday	8400
Wednesday	6200

a How many more points did he score on Tuesday than on Monday? [ ]

b What was his total score for Monday and Wednesday? [ ]

c How many more points does he need to reach 20 000 points in total? [ ]

6

Answer these.

Use a bar model to help represent each problem.

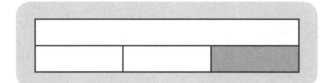

a A jug that holds 3500 ml is partly filled with 2650 ml of juice. How much more juice needs to be added to the jug to fill it?

ml

b What is the difference in mass between two parcels weighing 4360 g and 2060 g?

g

c A fisherman catches 2 fish weighing a total of 6300 g. The heavier fish has a mass of 3800 g. What is the mass of the other fish?

g

d 7800 ml of hot water is put into a tub for washing. A further 640 ml of cold water is added to cool it down. How much water is in the tub in total?

ml

e 6200 g of rice is poured into three bags. The first bag has 1900 g of rice in it and the second bag has double that amount. What is the mass of the rice in the third bag?

g

f A farmer sold 2000 litres of milk in Week 1 and 1150 litres in Week 2. In the third week he sold 250 litres less than in Week 1. What was the total amount of milk sold in those 3 weeks?

l

g To make some concrete, 6300 g of sand is mixed with 9800 g of cement. 1500 g of the mixture is used for a path. What is the mass of the mixture that remains?

g

h Three pipes laid end to end have a total length of 4700 cm. Two of the pipes are the same length and the other shorter pipe is 1500 cm long. What is the length of each of the 2 longer pipes?

cm

Decimals and fractions in real life

12a Equivalences

1 Write the equivalent fractions shown on each fraction bar.

a

0   1

$$\frac{2}{\boxed{}} = \frac{1}{\boxed{}}$$

b

0   1

$$\frac{5}{\boxed{}} = \frac{1}{\boxed{}}$$

c

0   1

$$\frac{8}{\boxed{}} = \frac{4}{\boxed{}}$$

d

0   1

$$\frac{3}{\boxed{}} = \frac{1}{\boxed{}}$$

e

0   1

$$\frac{5}{\boxed{}} = \frac{1}{\boxed{}}$$

f

0   1

$$\frac{10}{\boxed{}} = \frac{2}{\boxed{}}$$

2 Complete these equivalent fraction chains.

a $\dfrac{1}{5} = \dfrac{\square}{10} = \dfrac{3}{\square} = \dfrac{\square}{20} = \dfrac{\square}{\square} = \dfrac{\square}{\square}$

b $\dfrac{1}{10} = \dfrac{2}{\square} = \dfrac{\square}{30} = \dfrac{4}{\square} = \dfrac{\square}{\square} = \dfrac{\square}{\square}$

c $\dfrac{1}{15} = \dfrac{2}{\square} = \dfrac{\square}{45} = \dfrac{4}{\square} = \dfrac{\square}{\square} = \dfrac{\square}{\square}$

d $\dfrac{1}{20} = \dfrac{\square}{40} = \dfrac{3}{\square} = \dfrac{\square}{80} = \dfrac{\square}{\square} = \dfrac{\square}{\square}$

3 Circle the fraction in each set that is **not** equivalent.

a $\dfrac{2}{10}$ $\quad \dfrac{1}{5}$ $\quad \dfrac{3}{9}$ $\quad \dfrac{4}{20}$

c $\dfrac{3}{30}$ $\quad \dfrac{1}{3}$ $\quad \dfrac{3}{9}$ $\quad \dfrac{5}{15}$

e $\dfrac{3}{24}$ $\quad \dfrac{1}{8}$ $\quad \dfrac{3}{16}$ $\quad \dfrac{4}{32}$

b $\dfrac{2}{12}$ $\quad \dfrac{1}{2}$ $\quad \dfrac{12}{24}$ $\quad \dfrac{6}{12}$

d $\dfrac{4}{16}$ $\quad \dfrac{6}{24}$ $\quad \dfrac{4}{20}$ $\quad \dfrac{1}{4}$

f $\dfrac{1}{4}$ $\quad \dfrac{3}{12}$ $\quad \dfrac{4}{16}$ $\quad \dfrac{3}{4}$

 4 Answer these.

a $3\frac{2}{5} + 4\frac{1}{5} = \boxed{}$

d $1\frac{3}{5} - \frac{2}{5} = \boxed{}$

b $1\frac{3}{10} + 2\frac{3}{10} = \boxed{}$

e $2\frac{7}{10} - 1\frac{3}{10} = \boxed{}$

c $5\frac{1}{15} + 3\frac{9}{15} = \boxed{}$

f $6\frac{11}{15} - 4\frac{7}{15} = \boxed{}$

5 Write both the common fraction and decimal fraction for each arrow.

a

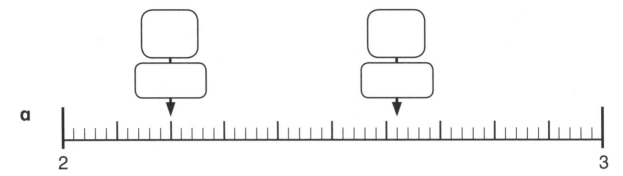

b

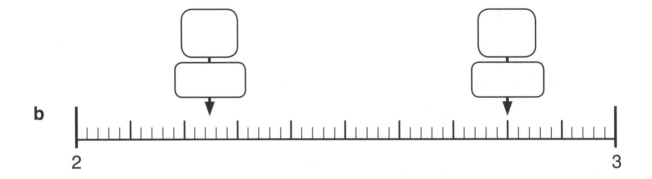

c

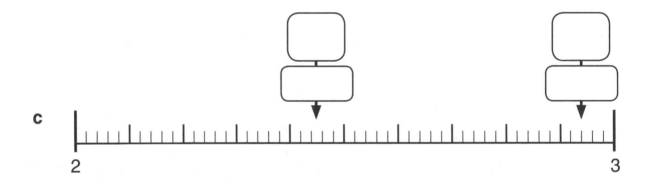

 Write these as equivalent fractions.

a $0.5 = \dfrac{5}{10} = \dfrac{\boxed{}}{2}$

c $0.8 = \dfrac{\boxed{}}{10} = \dfrac{\boxed{}}{5}$

e $0.75 = \dfrac{\boxed{}}{100} = \dfrac{\boxed{}}{4}$

b $0.6 = \dfrac{\boxed{}}{10} = \dfrac{\boxed{}}{5}$

d $0.25 = \dfrac{\boxed{}}{100} = \dfrac{\boxed{}}{4}$

f $0.02 = \dfrac{\boxed{}}{100} = \dfrac{\boxed{}}{50}$

7

Play this game in pairs.

One-tenth	One-fifth	Three-tenths	Two-fifths	One-half
Three-fifths	Seven-tenths	Four-fifths	Nine-tenths	One
0.1	0.2	0.3	0.4	0.5
0.6	0.7	0.8	0.9	1

To play:

- Shuffle the 20 cards and place them in a pile face down.

- Take turns to turn the top card over.

- Place a counter on the number track to match the card turned over.

- If there is already a counter on the number, remove that counter.

- Once the 20 cards have been turned over, shuffle them and start from the top again.

- The winner is the first player to get 3 of their counters in a row

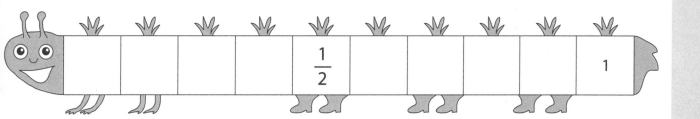

12b Comparing and rounding decimals

1 Complete this chart.

	tens	ones	.	tenths	hundredths
27.8	2	7	.		
2.78			.		
12.78			.		
12.8			.		
1.28			.		
12.08			.		

2 Write the decimal number each arrow points to.

a

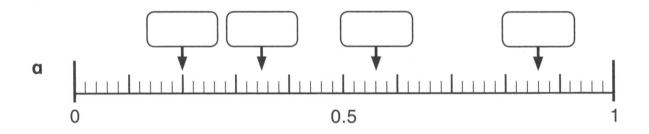

b

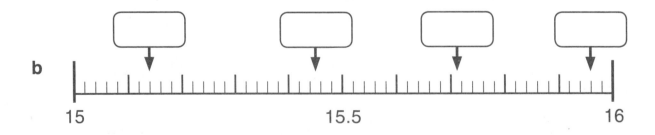

3 Write < or > between these numbers. Use the number lines on page 112 to help you.

a 0.6 ⬚ 0.3   e 15.05 ⬚ 15.1

b 0.9 ⬚ 0.18   f 15.62 ⬚ 15.29

c 0.75 ⬚ 0.8   g 15.9 ⬚ 15.93

d 0.12 ⬚ 0.35   h 15.56 ⬚ 15.7

4 Write each set of numbers in order. Use the signs < or >. Start with the smallest.

a
17.47 17.45 17.5

⬚ ⬚ ⬚

c
0.93 0.09 0.08

⬚ ⬚ ⬚

b
28.93 20.84 28.92

⬚ ⬚ ⬚

d
77.44 7.94 7.49

⬚ ⬚ ⬚

Start with the largest.

e
27.21 27.25 27.52

⬚ ⬚ ⬚

g
29.23 29.4 29.38

⬚ ⬚ ⬚

f
14.67 14.7 14.69

⬚ ⬚ ⬚

h
4.09 40.9 4.9

⬚ ⬚ ⬚

5 This chart shows the height and mass of a group of people.

	Anna	Ben	Craig	Diane	Ethan	Fiona
Height (m)	1.63	1.67	1.79	1.7	1.81	1.71
Mass (kg)	81.29	79.85	87.37	70.61	87.15	74.62

a Write the heights in order, starting with the tallest.

[ ] [ ] [ ] [ ] [ ] [ ]

b Write the masses in order, starting with the heaviest.

[ ] [ ] [ ] [ ] [ ] [ ]

 6 Join each decimal to the nearest tenth on the number line.

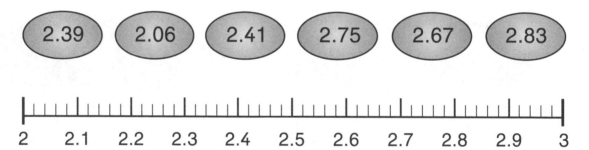

 7 Round each amount to the nearest whole number.

a 28.6 cm ➜ [cm]   **d** 27.5 g ➜ [g]

b 5.82 litres ➜ [litres]   **e** 12.08 km ➜ [km]

c £84.49 ➜ [ ]   **f** 4.56 kg ➜ [kg]

8 Round each amount to the nearest tenth.

a £7.07 ➔ ☐   **d** 9.88 kg ➔ [kg]

b 8.34 litres ➔ [litres]   **e** 42.39 km ➔ [km]

c 19.51 m ➔ [m]   **f** £35.54 ➔ ☐

9 Rearrange this set of digits to make 6 different decimal numbers between 1 and 10.

Use each digit only once in each decimal number.

a

b Write the decimal numbers you have made in order, starting with the smallest.

smallest ➔

☐.☐☐

Multiplication tables

 1 Write in the missing numbers to complete this multiplication square.

×	0	1	2	3	4	5	6	7	8	9	10	11	12
0	0	0		0	0			0	0	0	0	0	0
1	0		2			5	6	7		9	10		12
2	0	2	4		8	10			16	18			
3		3		9	12			21			30	33	36
4	0	4	8				24		32	36			
5	0	5		15		25	30			45	50	55	60
6	0	6	12		24			42	48		60	66	
7	0	7			28	35				63		77	
8		8		24		40		56			80	88	96
9	0			27	36		54		72	81	90		108
10		10	20	30	40	50	60		80		100		
11			22	33	44	55			88		110	121	
12		12	24		48		72		96		120		

Colour the square for each of these.

1 × 1   2 × 2   3 × 3   4 × 4   5 × 5   6 × 6

7 × 7   8 × 8   9 × 9   10 × 10   11 × 11   12 × 12

What do you notice?

2 Answer each set as quickly as you can.

a

2 × 3 =

2 × 6 =

4 × 6 =

8 × 6 =

8 × 3 =

4 × 3 =

4 × 4 =

8 × 8 =

8 × 7 =

7 × 7 =

b

3 × 5 =

6 × 5 =

12 × 5 =

12 × 10 =

12 × 11 =

6 × 11 =

3 × 11 =

9 × 11 =

9 × 12 =

12 × 12 =

c

21 ÷ 3 =

21 ÷ 7 =

42 ÷ 7 =

42 ÷ 6 =

48 ÷ 6 =

48 ÷ 12 =

48 ÷ 4 =

24 ÷ 4 =

24 ÷ 3 =

12 ÷ 3 =

d

30 ÷ 5 =

60 ÷ 5 =

60 ÷ 12 =

30 ÷ 6 =

15 ÷ 3 =

45 ÷ 9 =

90 ÷ 9 =

70 ÷ 7 =

63 ÷ 7 =

63 ÷ 9 =

3 Look at the abacus then complete the sentences.

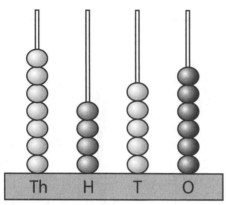

a 30 more than 7456 is

d 200 less than 7456 is

b 50 less than 7456 is

e 2000 more than 7456 is

c 400 more than 7456 is

f 6000 less than 7456 is

4 Count in these steps. Write the missing numbers.

a Count on in 300s starting from 4280

b Count on in 2000s starting from 1058

c Count on in 50s starting from 2840

d Count on in 25s starting from 1700

5 The score on this dartboard is 38.

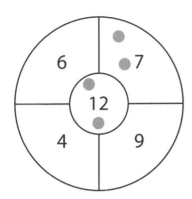

$2 \times 7 = 14$

$2 \times 12 = 24$

Total ➜ 38

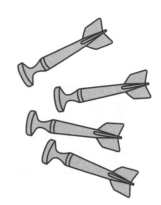

Write these total scores.

a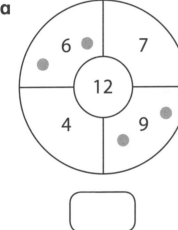

b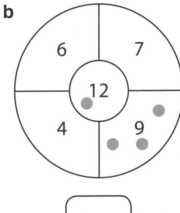

c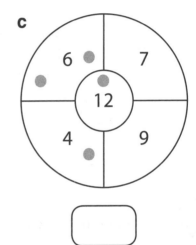

Investigate the different totals you can make on this dartboard with 4 darts.

6 Use the digits 1 to 9.

| 1 | 2 | 3 | 4 | 5 | 6 | 7 | 8 | 9 |

Find a place for each digit:

◻ × 8 = 2◻

◻ × 7 = 4◻

2 × ◻ = ◻◻

◻ × 4 = ◻0

13b Multiplying on paper

1 Complete these.

a 285 × 3 = ☐

×	200	80	5
3			

c 538 × 7 = ☐

×	500	30	8
7			

b 479 × 5 = ☐

×	400	70	9
5			

d 653 × 9 = ☐

×	600	50	3
9			

2 Answer these. Estimate the answer first.

a
```
    394     Estimate:
×     3     400 × 3 = ?
  ────
```
☐

d
```
    195     Estimate:
×     8
  ────
```
☐

b
```
    237     Estimate:
×     5     200 × 5 = ?
  ────
```
☐

e
```
    673     Estimate:
×     6
  ────
```
☐

c
```
    608     Estimate:
×     4
  ────
```
☐

f
```
    571     Estimate:
×     9
  ────
```
☐

3 Work out the total mass for each of these.

a

Coffee 395 g Coffee 395 g Coffee 395 g Coffee 395 g Coffee 395 g Coffee 395 g

Total mass = [　　　] g

b

RICE 685 g RICE 685 g RICE 685 g

Total mass = [　　　] g

c

Flour 840 g Flour 840 g Flour 840 g Flour 840 g Flour 840 g

Total mass = [　　　] g

d

Sugar 735 g Sugar 735 g Sugar 735 g Sugar 735 g Sugar 735 g Sugar 735 g Sugar 735 g

Total mass = [　　　] g

4 Use these digits.

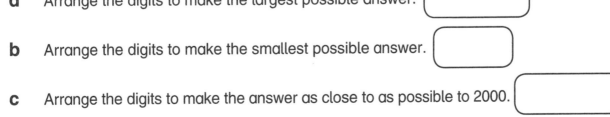

5 4 2 9

[　][　][　]

× [　]

_____

a Arrange the digits to make the largest possible answer. [　　　]

b Arrange the digits to make the smallest possible answer. [　　　]

c Arrange the digits to make the answer as close to as possible to 2000. [　　　]

1 Write the value of the unknown number in the shaded box.

a
60		

e
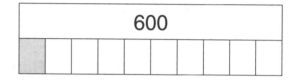

	600		

b
60					

f
	600							

c
60			

g
	60			

d
60						

h
	600									

What do you notice?

2 Answer these.

a What number is 20 times larger than 6?

b What number is 100 times larger than 6?

c What number is 50 times larger than 10?

d What number is 200 times larger than 10?

e What number is 10 times smaller than 100?

f What number is 20 times smaller than 100?

g What number is 100 times smaller than 300?

h What number is 50 times smaller than 300?

3 Solve these problems. Draw bar models to help you answer them.

a Sam collects stickers and has 5 times as many as Lizzie. If Lizzie has 30 stickers, how many stickers do they have altogether?

b A model car is 20 times shorter than the real car, which is 360 centimetres in length. What is the length of the model?

c A recipe for a pie for 4 people uses 220 g of flour. How much flour would be needed to make a pie for 12 people?

d A book costs 4 times the price of a magazine. Together they cost £10. What is the cost of the magazine?

4 An optician sells glasses which give his customers three choices: style, colour and size.

When the shop opened in January, there were only 2 styles, 2 colours and 1 size to choose from.

a How many different choices did the shop offer in January?

Month	Style	Colour	Size	Number of different pairs of glasses
January	2	2	1	

b The optician decided to increase his range each month.
Complete this chart to show the different choices the shop offers.

Month	Style	Colour	Size	Number of different pairs of glasses
February	2	2	2	
March	3	2	2	
April	4	3	2	
May	4	3	3	
June	4	4	4	

What do you notice?

Perimeter, area and symmetry

1 Calculate the area of each rectangle.

a
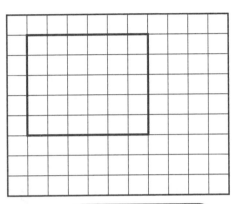

Area = [ ] squares

d
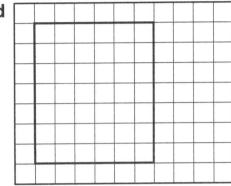

Area = [ ] squares

b
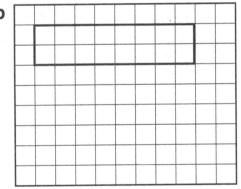

Area = [ ] squares

e
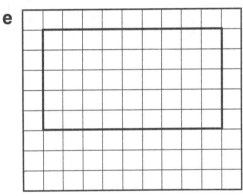

Area = [ ] squares

c
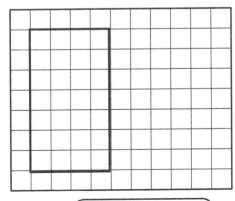

Area = [ ] squares

f
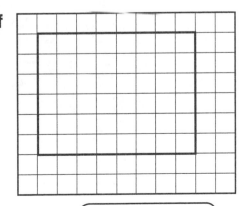

Area = [ ] squares

2 Write the perimeter for each garden.

a

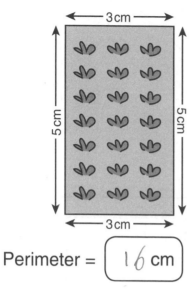

3 cm (top)
5 cm (left)
5 cm (right)
3 cm (bottom)

Perimeter = ☐ 16 cm

b

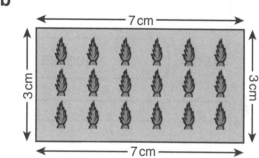

7 cm (top)
3 cm (left)
3 cm (right)
7 cm (bottom)

Perimeter = ☐ 20 cm

c

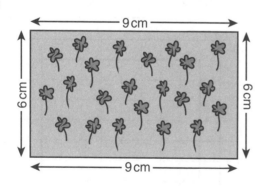

9 cm (top)
6 cm (left)
6 cm (right)
9 cm (bottom)

Perimeter = ☐ 30 cm

d

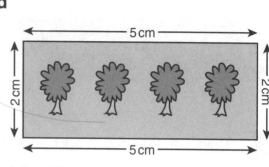

5 cm (top)
2 cm (left)
2 cm (right)
5 cm (bottom)

Perimeter = ☐ 14 cm

e

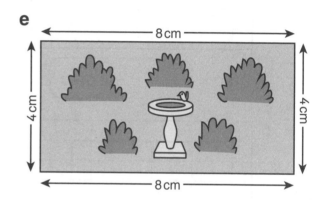

8 cm (top)
4 cm (left)
4 cm (right)
8 cm (bottom)

Perimeter = ☐ 24 cm

f

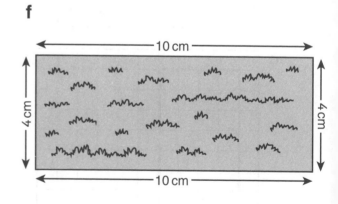

10 cm (top)
4 cm (left)
4 cm (right)
10 cm (bottom)

Perimeter = ☐ 28 cm

3 What is the area and perimeter of each of these? Each small square is 1 cm².

a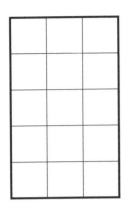

Perimeter = [　　　] cm

Area = [　　　] cm²

d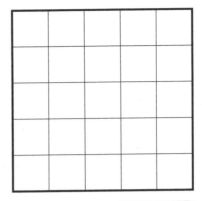

Perimeter = [　　　] cm

Area = [　　　] cm²

b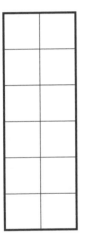

Perimeter = [　　　] cm

Area = [　　　] cm²

e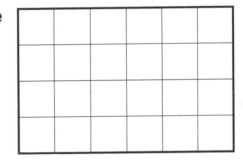

Perimeter = [　　　] cm

Area = [　　　] cm²

c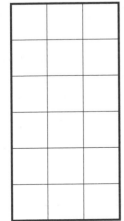

Perimeter = [　　　] cm

Area = [　　　] cm²

4   This table shows the lengths and widths of different rectangles.

Complete the table to show the area and perimeter of each rectangle.

Length	Width	Area (length × width)	Perimeter 2 (length + width)
2 cm	3 cm	cm²	cm
4 cm	6 cm	cm²	cm
4 cm	7 cm	cm²	cm
7 cm	7 cm	cm²	cm
5 cm	5 cm	cm²	cm
5 cm	10 cm	cm²	cm
10 cm	10 cm	cm²	cm
20 cm	5 cm	cm²	cm

 5   Answer these.

a   The area of a square is 64 cm².
What is the length of each side?

cm

b   The perimeter of a square is 96 cm.
What is the length of each side?

cm

 6   Patrick is given a vegetable plot with an area of 24 square metres. He is allowed to have any rectangle shape for his plot but each side must be a whole number of metres.

Investigate the different shapes he could have for his vegetable plot.

a   Which rectangle gives him the greatest perimeter?

b   Which rectangle gives him the smallest perimeter?

1 Calculate the perimeter of each shape.

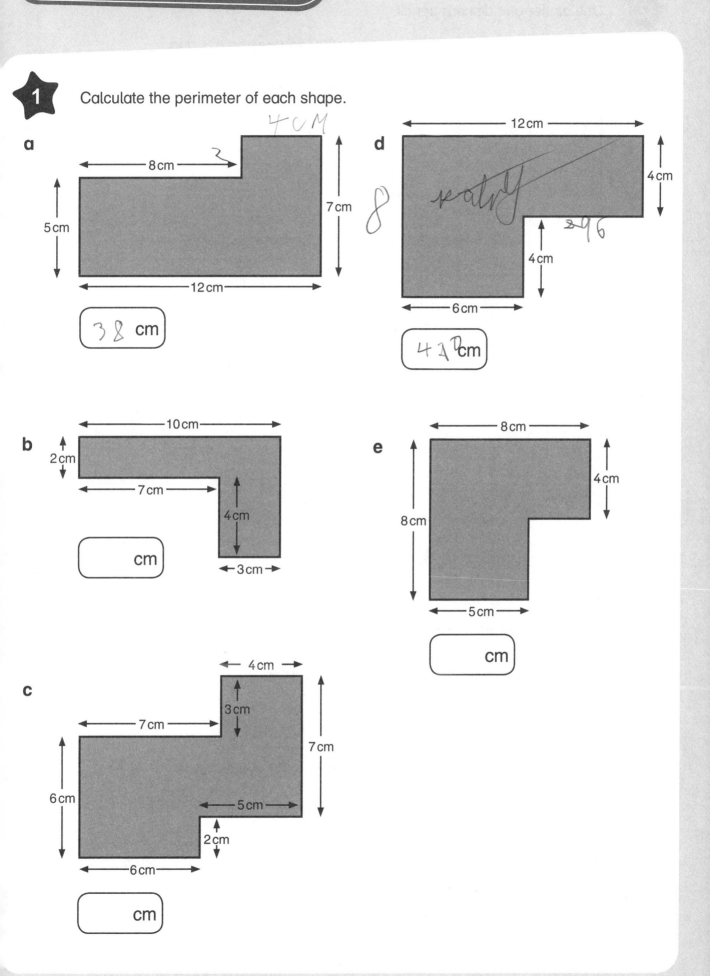

a

8 cm
4 cm
5 cm
7 cm
12 cm

38 cm

b

10 cm
2 cm
7 cm
4 cm
3 cm

cm

c

4 cm
3 cm
7 cm
7 cm
6 cm
5 cm
2 cm
6 cm

cm

d

12 cm
4 cm
katy
4 cm
6 cm

42 cm

e

8 cm
8 cm
4 cm
5 cm

cm

2 Use a ruler and a sharp pencil.

Draw a rectilinear shape with an area of 20 squares on this grid.

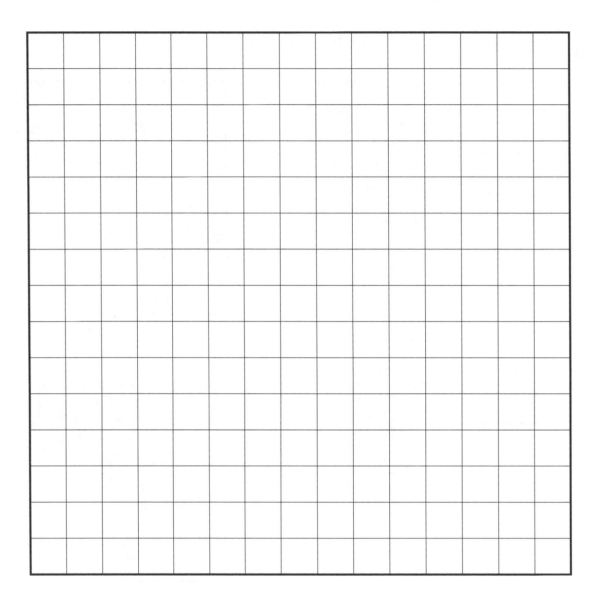

a Measure and record the perimeter of your shape.

[ ] cm

b Can you draw another shape with the same area but a larger perimeter?

c Now try to draw a shape with the same area but a smaller perimeter.

3 Take a piece of rough paper. Fold it to make a straight line. Fold it again to make a right angle checker.

Write **acute**, **obtuse** or **right angle** in the grid for each angle.

Use your right angle checker to help you.

a    e

b    f

c    g

d    h

a	
b	
c	
d	
e	
f	
g	
h	

4 Look at these 6 angles.

Write them in order of size, starting with the smallest.

A    D

B   E

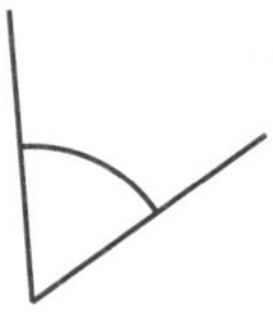

C   F

5 For each shape write the number of **acute** angles, **obtuse** angles and **right angles**.

a

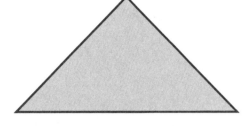

- ☐ acute angles
- ☐ obtuse angles
- ☐ right angles

d

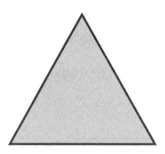

- ☐ acute angles
- ☐ obtuse angles
- ☐ right angles

b

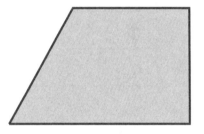

- ☐ acute angles
- ☐ obtuse angles
- ☐ right angles

e

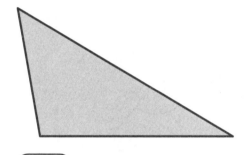

- ☐ acute angles
- ☐ obtuse angles
- ☐ right angles

c

- ☐ acute angles
- ☐ obtuse angles
- ☐ right angles

f

- ☐ acute angles
- ☐ obtuse angles
- ☐ right angles

6 Draw shapes made from whole squares on this grid.
Record their area and perimeter.

Perimeter = 8 cm   Perimeter = 8 cm

Area = 3 cm²   Area = 4 cm²

Try to find shapes with the same perimeter but different areas.

14c Area and symmetry

1 What is the area of each rectangle?

a
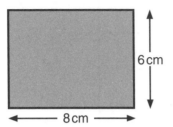
6 cm
8 cm

c
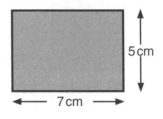
5 cm
7 cm

e
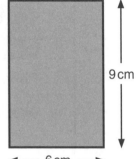
9 cm
6 cm

b
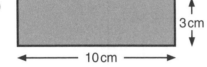
3 cm
10 cm

d
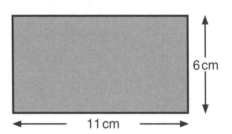
6 cm
11 cm

2 Look at this grid.

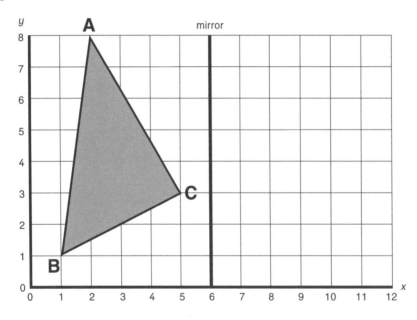

a What are the coordinates of the vertices of the triangle?

A (⬚ , ⬚) B (⬚ , ⬚) C (⬚ , ⬚)

b Draw the reflection of the triangle in the mirror line.

c What are the coordinates of the vertices of the reflected triangle?

(⬚ , ⬚) (⬚ , ⬚) (⬚ , ⬚)

3 Plot these coordinates on the grid below:

A (2, 5)   **B** (4, 5)   **C** (2, 7)   **D** (5, 8)

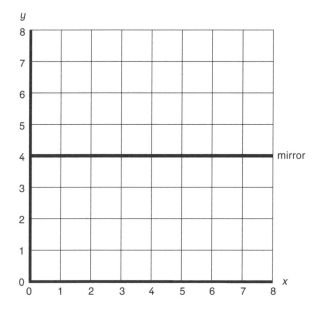

a   Join the coordinates with a ruler to make a quadrilateral.

b   Draw the reflection of the quadrilateral in the mirror.

c   Write the coordinates of the vertices of the reflected quadrilateral.

( ,) (,) (,) (,)

4　Shade squares on the other side of the line to make the pattern symmetrical.

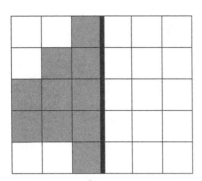

Make up your own symmetrical patterns like this. Use colour and shape in your symmetrical patterns.

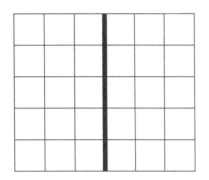
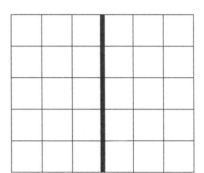

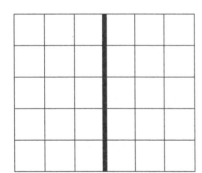
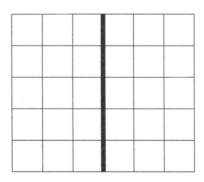

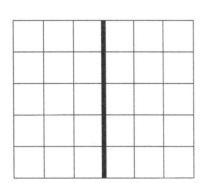
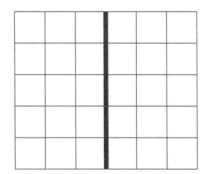

Compare the area of each of your patterns.

Which has the greatest area? Which has the smallest area?

5 Draw each shape on this Carroll diagram.

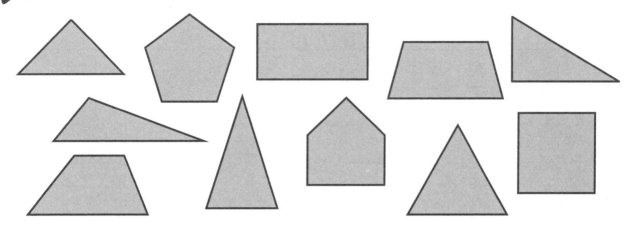

	Symmetrical	Not symmetrical
Some right angles		
No right angles		

My jottings

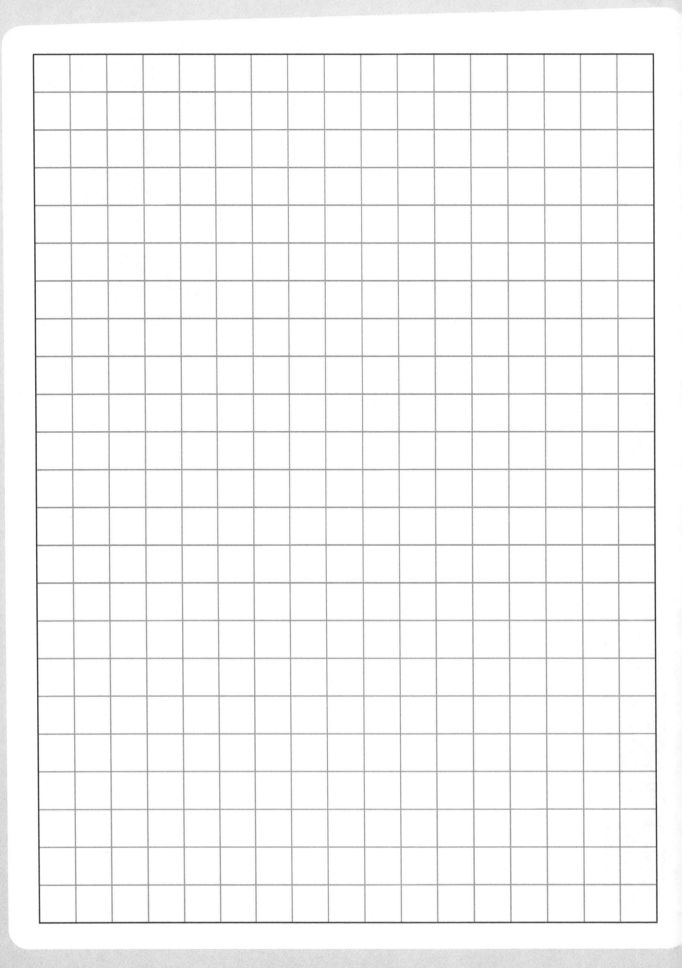

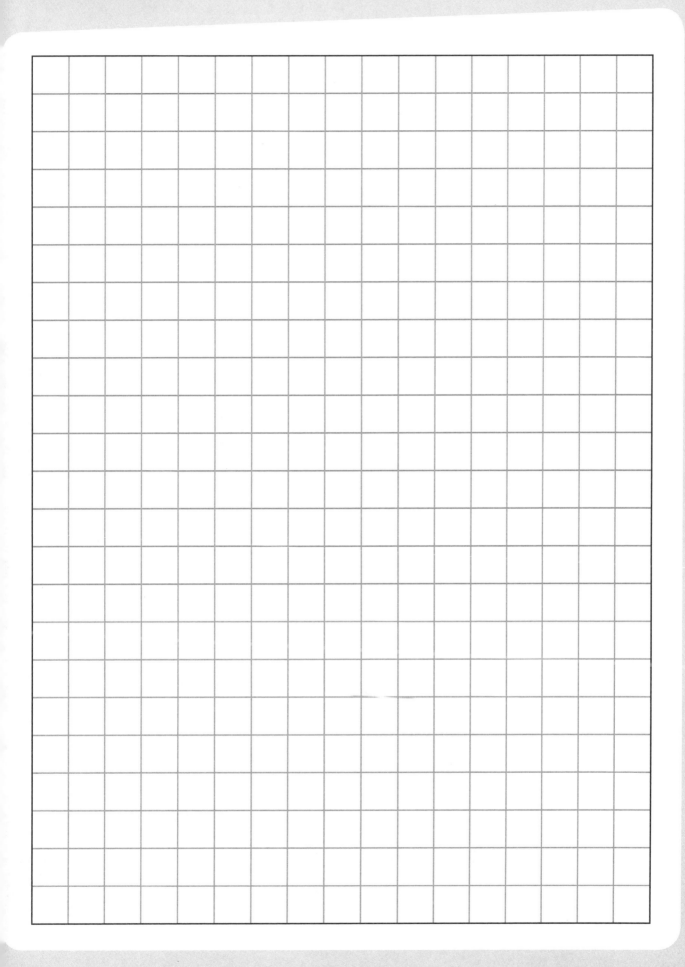

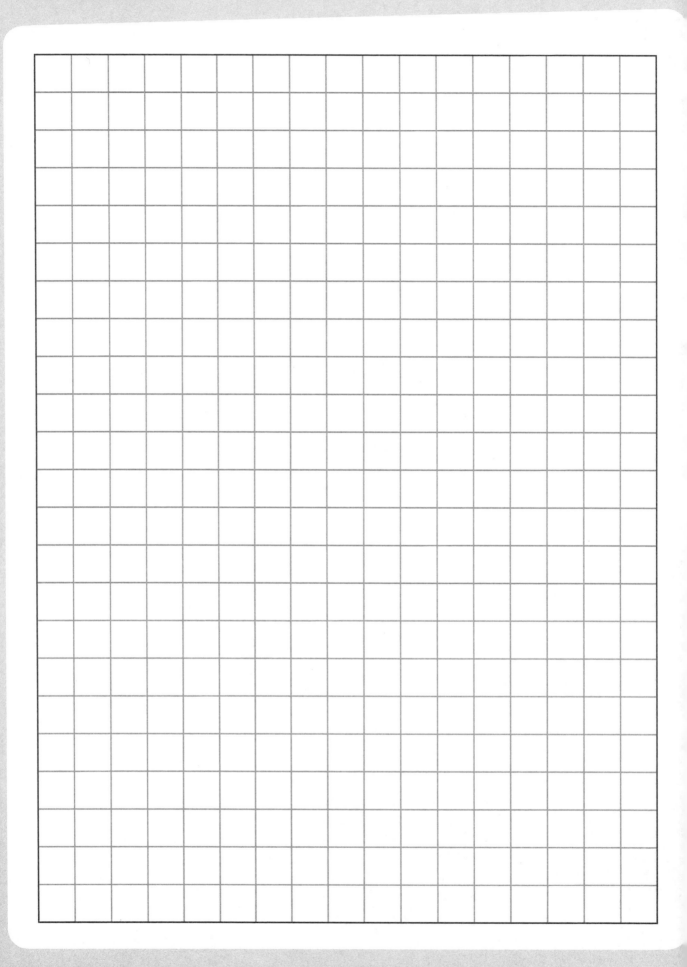

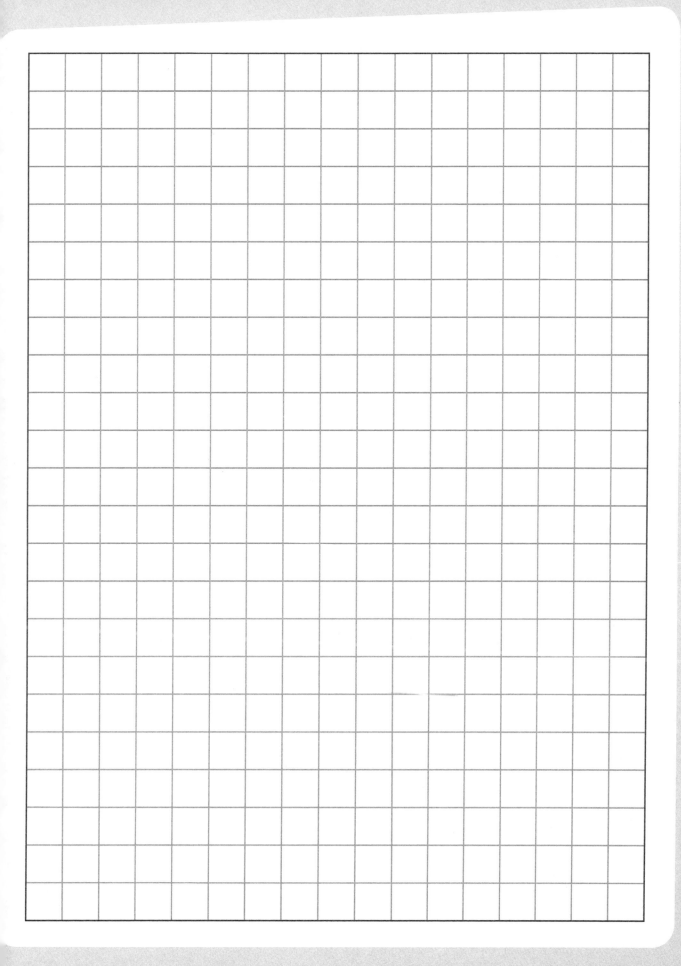

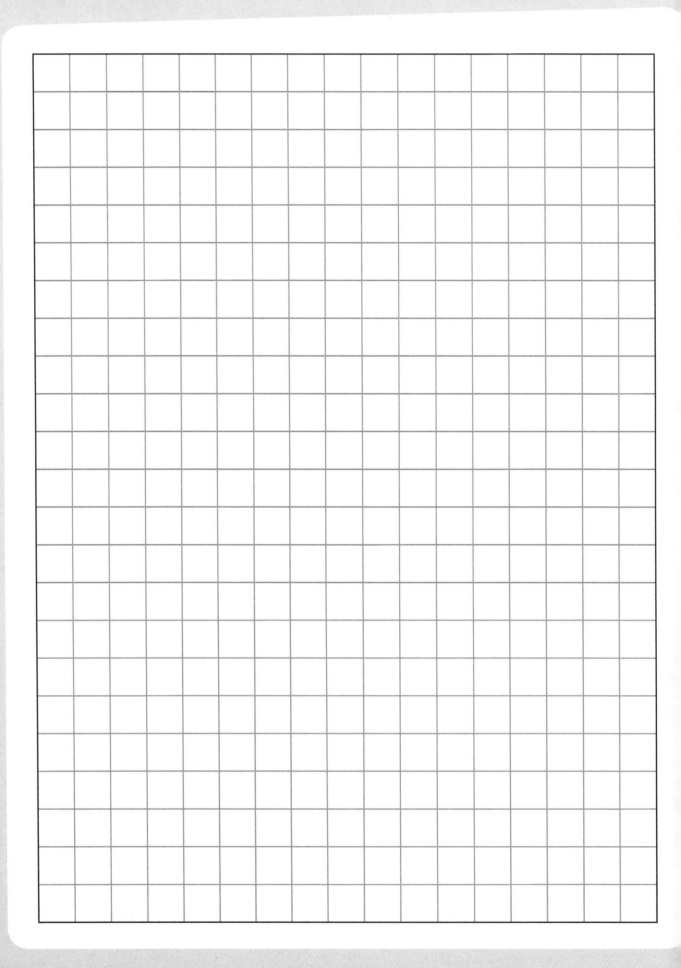

My jottings

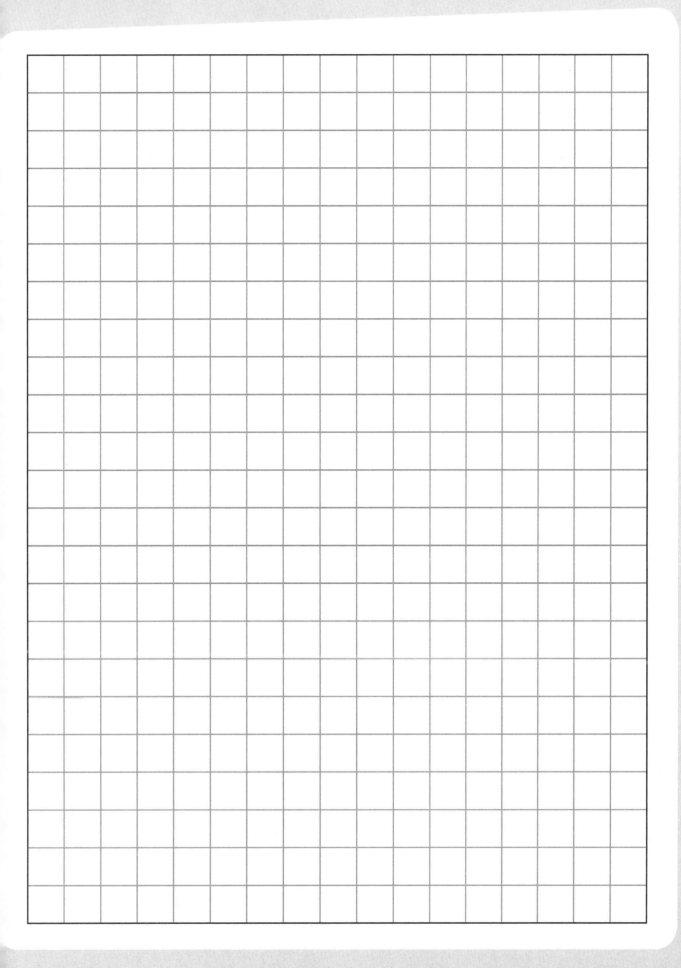

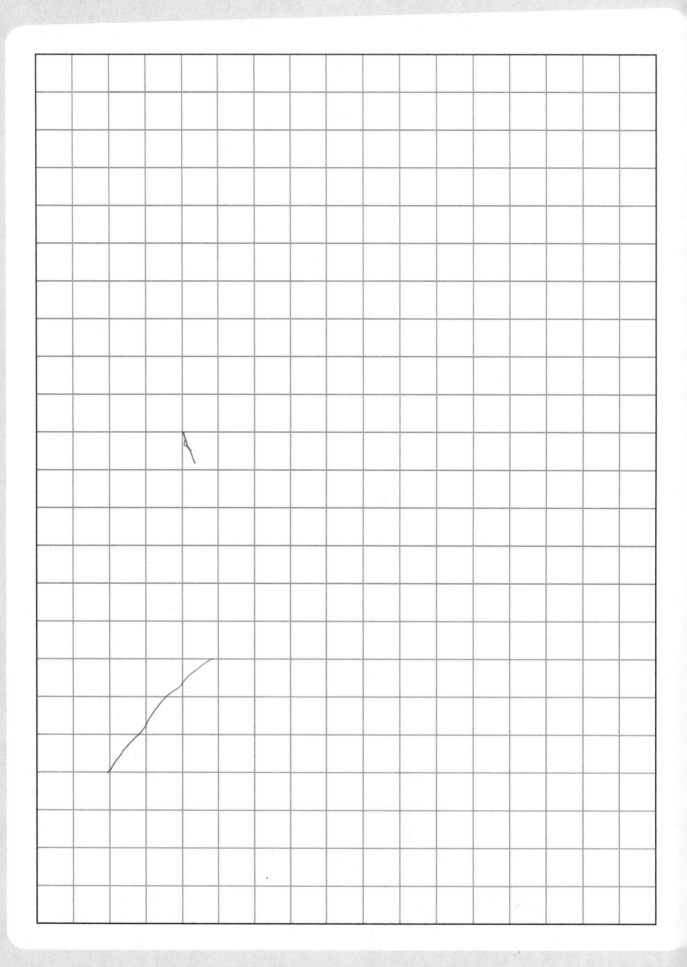